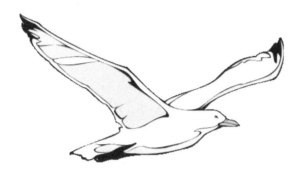

As your own year unfolds,
ponder our four-century
HISTORY
of women and men in
America.

ALSO BY LAURA EMERSON DUNN

Nine for Hillary: A 2016 Union of American Ancestors

ARRIVAL 2020

LAURA EMERSON DUNN

Dedication

To my *Mayflower* grandparents

Elizabeth and Richard Warren
Barbara and Myles Standish
Ann and Henry Samson
Elizabeth and William Mullins
Priscilla and John Alden

and to my grandchildren

Wyatt J Dunn
and
Jessa Louise Dunn

Acknowledgements

Picture your own Plymouth, Massachusetts, visit to Plimoth Plantation in 2020 or beyond. Might you be greeted by Co-Director Richard Pickering, as was my good fortune in 2017, 2018, and 2019? Regardless, you will have the opportunity to witness the re-created 1670 Warren House site, in progress or complete. To my fellow Warren descendant, for his vision and execution of this memorial to businesswoman and landowner Elizabeth Warren (1583-1673) and her family, I could not be more grateful. I extend also warm thanks to Cousin Richard's Executive Assistant Tom Begley, and to interns from Bridgewater State, for their amazing Warren Project research, which helps to inform my recounting of Elizabeth's story in *ARRIVAL 2020*.

Picture also your own Duxbury visit to the Bradford House in 2020 or beyond. Perhaps it will be your good luck, as it has been mine, to find the docent on site to be Carolyn Ravenscroft. Her decade as Historian and Archivist for the Duxbury Rural and Historical Society has yielded, among other treasures, this memorial to 19th century Bradford sisters Maria, Lucia, Elizabeth and Charlotte. Those abolitionist, suffragist, *Mayflower*-descended women shared the acquaintance and passions of *ARRIVAL 2020's* Louisa May Alcott (1832-1888). Many thanks to Carolyn for bringing the Bradford sisters to life in 21st century Duxbury, and to Director Erin McGough, to Carly Olson, Sabrina Kaplan, Peter Donohoe, Melanie Correia, and a long list of others, for keeping the DRHS alive and thriving. Their resources have been a priceless aid to my efforts.

Imagine yourself on a Massachusetts byway in Kingston, Rocky Nook to be exact, where *Mayflower* passengers Elizabeth Tilley and her husband John Howland (luckily for millions of descendants, John survived a spill overboard, saved by a trailing halyard) settled after 1640, when Master Howland had sold off his 80 acres in Duxbury. John used the Colony's refitted shallop, perhaps same as the one in which he'd survived a 1620 near-shipwreck at Clark's Island, to trade up and down the northern Atlantic seaboard. Might descendant Peter Arenstam, 21st century overseer of construction of the recreated, refitted boat now named the *Elizabeth Tilley*, happen to drive by on an otherwise deserted stretch of road? For me, that one-in-a-million chance occurred in 2017, occasioning my first face-to-face meeting with the man who now serves as Executive Director of the Pilgrim John Howland Society. In 2020, you too will be able to meet him at the Jabez Howland House in Plymouth, to learn more of the fascinating history of women and men in America, starting in 1620.

Thank you, Peter Arenstam and Jon Daley, Howland descendants who, for five other eager passengers heading for Clark's Island in August 2019 on the *Elizabeth Tilley*, so ably crewed alongside captain Michael Goldstein, whose descendant wife Joanne Pratt was onboard as well. That opportunity to savor sun, salt air, and sea gulls soaring overhead, under sail in Plymouth Bay, provided a priceless trip back in time for this author.

To Gail Adams, heartfelt appreciation for the PJHS Quarterly newsletter so skillfully edited, and for an ongoing effort to convince the old guard to include Elizabeth Tilley's name in the title of your society. I shall claim near certainty that Franklin Delano Roosevelt, your cousin as fellow descendant of *Mayflower* passenger Elizabeth Tilley, would approve. No doubt spouse Eleanor, known as a 20th century political leader in her own right, would be onboard.

Since made available to the public in 1907, millions have visited the Alden House in Duxbury, built circa 1672 for the benefit of Jonathan, son of Priscilla and John Alden. You, too, might enjoy that thrill in 2020 or beyond, might be greeted by Director Desiree Mobed, and further educated by a tour guide on the lives of women and men, or girls and boys, who once set foot on the very same floor boards where you tread. Joy, my one fictional character in *ARRIVAL 2020*, sends her gratitude to Desiree and to Alden Kindred President Pauline Kezer, as do I, for keeping this history safely alive and well.

Fellow Alden descendant Loree Kerr, words cannot express, yet I shall try. Your birth as Katherine Ann Soule, descended from *Mayflower* passenger George Soule and wife Mary Becket, remained a mystery unknown to you until a few short years before April 2019, when we discovered one another. Subsequent to our "meeting," you became the perfect editor and formatter for this project, as well as added inspiration and beloved eighth cousin. It is not hyperbole to say that I could not have done this without you.

For my accomplished, endlessly supportive son, daughter-in-law, and daughter, mountains of loving gratitude. Thank you also, Kyla Dunn, for so many decades gifting me the latest and best books related to our favorite American pioneer, Laura Ingalls Wilder (1867-1957). Mary Emerson Smith and Kathy Emerson, love and thanks for cheering me on. Our Mom and Dad, who never knew of our *Mayflower* descent, would be amused for themselves and pleased for their three daughters ("the girls") and three sons ("the boys"). To Ned and Warren, and to Bill Emerson who cares for Mom as she fades away, my appreciation and love for my little brothers knows no bounds.

To relatives of subjects Dorothea Brande, Sarah Wingate Taylor, and Cid Ricketts Sumner, I owe enormous thanks. Gil Collins, Skip Taylor, and Meg Cutler Chandler, you have been so kind and generous with your time and heartfelt memories of your mother, aunt, and grandmother.

To the many who, however briefly or at length, have read, listened to and discussed many aspects of this history of women and men in America, Roger Boyer, Tanya Sydney, and Susan Kinsella among them, profound thanks are due. For inspiration from fellow book lovers in my Stanford book group in Marin, not limited to but including Christine Salesky, Claire Venezia, Bonnie Seto-Myers, Kasey Arnold-

Ince, Gilda Turitz, Faye Kelly, Karlyn Carnahan, Christina Kranenburg, and Patricia Prince, I remain forever grateful.

My gratitude to dear sisters-in-law Laura Perani Emerson and the Reverend Deacon Mary Beth Emerson of Trinity Church, Marshfield, who supports Warren's return to an extraordinary hometown, as he comes to realize, "Duxbury is in my DNA." I extend to Robyn Simonett of capslockon.com, craniosacral chiropractor Greg Crossman, and Duxbury realtor and friend Donna Wood, who made it possible for me to reside in 2020 on land once owned by 17th century ancestors, my warmest appreciation. For dozens more in the "you know who you are" category, there is a grateful place in my heart.

CONTENTS

1620

APPROACHING WINTER SOLSTICE, AT DUSK. Terrified travelers, pitching midst howling wind, freezing in snowy sleet, adrift under darkening sky, fear their days are done. For saintly souls, visions of leaving Leyden for England, then England for safe haven in America appear doomed to be dashed on a rocky shore. All tremble, some moan, in the face of final moments.

Gray seas roil. Eighteen bodies in the battered vessel hurl skyward, then drop down towering waves toward bottom of forbidding bay. Men call out names of loved ones, while night lowers her ebony cape.

Seven dozen fellow specks of humanity wait at Provincetown harbor, where the Mayflower had found her way to this great Atlantic seaboard. Will an arduous ocean voyage, inspired by decades of striving for religious freedom, yield terror-stricken ending for their scouting party? Must those who now wait make do without them? Are carefully chosen emissaries, beaten and broken by boulders, headed to watery grave?

Eight are Mayflower crew, ten passengers. Of the ten, six term themselves "saints." The other four, and their like, they call "stranger." Belief in their own pure image of God has tightly bound the two Tilley brothers to Ed Winslow, Governor Carver, his servant John Howland, and to a young visionary named William Bradford.

A less complex rationale drives merchant Richard Warren, militant Myles Standish, adventurer Stephen Hopkins, and his servant Ted

Doty. There is land aplenty in this new world, awaiting inspired mercenaries.

This all-white, all-male boatload, launched from the mother ship, is in search of a proper spot to settle before December's end. The ocean floor is not what any of these men have in mind, for themselves or their shallop.

Unbeknownst to now desperate explorers, a female presence is about to make her mark. Someone, or Something, must save the day. But how to turn this terror to joy?

JOY 1

I WAS BORN TO LUNA in1620. Right here on Clark's Island, two days after a near shipwreck. This, and more, those of you gathered here have come to know.

Not long after, in this same sacred space, Mother and I returned for her final chapter. It was 1638 and time for her passing. It was time for finished tales, in Luna's wondrous words, of worlds of women to come. Much more I must know, prior to my choice.

Would I become a Goodwife then, as my eighteenth birthday neared? Or rise to witness with you, flying forward over four centuries in time?

Now in 2019 I stand before my fellow travelers, hearing more of your female lives. Hearing tender stories too, of men and boys you knew. I tell tales from my own early years of living. Together we commit to unearthing sometimes painful truths. I speak, again, as Luna fills my heart. My feathered friend, Shadow Seagull, he plays his stalwart part.

We found Anne first in 1643, Cid last in 1970, with fourteen others through the centuries joining, each at the point of her passing. From 1971 forward, over forty-nine years more we have pondered at these annual August gatherings. You sixteen women with Shadow and me, at the foot of Pulpit Rock, inspire rich recountings of challenges staunchly met. From distant past to present, the stage has now been set.

What to do about the state of *all* women and men in twenty-first century America? A 2020 world is in store, ahead on golden horizon. A future America beckons. But in 1638, how for me to decide? What lessons would guide me, Luna's daughter, when Mother departed this earth?

Now more of that story I shall recall. Let us reopen window shutters, once shielding my earliest, secret memories. Join me, again, in a jaunt to our past, with swift travels forward through history recast.

"Over twenty *Mayflower* passengers were female, you say, of one hundred and three. Why did not the ladies join in signing of the Compact?" When I was young, Mother chuckled often at such questions. "Out of the mouths of babes," Luna murmured.

Yes, history claims just one hundred and two 1620 passengers. By the eighteen hundreds, all were termed "Pilgrims." In November of 1863, Abraham Lincoln, while leading a nation through bloody civil war, would declare an annual day of thanks. "We gather together," many Americans now sing on Thanksgiving Day. The country honors brave *Mayflower* ancestors, worshippers of a mighty male God. Historians did not know, or care, about my mother Luna.

It was she who gave me a firsthand account of saving the day at this isle. There were ten saints and strangers, all set to rise in fame. During a shrieking and howling storm, self-reverent males begged mercy of their God. When saved, they gave eternal credit to the masculine Lord each so resembled.

Those scouting party survivors came to agree that a saving of the day by their righteous God seemed proof that their pilgrimage was wise and just. Bradford, Carver, Doty, Hopkins, Howland, Standish, both Tilleys, Warren, and Winslow. All were immigrant Englishmen, bearing ancient religious beliefs, and bringing cold, hard confidence in Christian culture from their homeland. This was a gift the "saints" imported for "new world" locals. Yet our determined explorers were hardly feckless fools. Perhaps dark-skinned inhabitants might hold a contrary view, those travelers knew.

Shipwreck-spared souls, saints and strangers alike, found new relief at dawn. No savages there on that newfound island. There were sighs of relief from strangers holding enhanced respect for the religious tenets of self-appointed saintly fellows. Things were looking up on their shared pilgrimage. No knowledge then of lady Luna's role.

A glorious morning followed a near-fatal night, Luna told me, with time to search the island and to repair their battered vessel. On day two, all rested and some worshiped by this glacial remnant, later christened Pulpit Rock. Solemn men held a first official Sabbath, endless miles from their motherland.

I was a persistent, pestering child, always eager to hear this and many stories more. "Tell me again about that name for the natives," I asked repeatedly. Luna (we all called her that) laughed each time, recounting tales of men like Amerigo Vespucci and Christopher Columbus. They'd known the world was round, and that India to the east could be reached by sailing west.

Of giant continents, looming large in between, said sailors had no knowledge. Soon, Mother explained, those lands came to bear Vespucci's name: America, North and South.

Meanwhile, "Indian" became our term for darker, "red-skinned" Squanto, who shared precious wisdom of old with the saints and strangers. From Squanto, our pale-skinned kind learned to plant blue corn with fish to nourish, with beans to climb the green stalks, and with broad-leaved orange squash to shade the soil below. A feast of thanks could be had that fall, visited by new native friends bearing gifts of tasty venison.

Luna told of an earlier capture of natives by the Englishman, Captain Hunt, who sailed to Spain and sold more than a dozen friends of Tisquantum. Mother sometimes used that full native name, when telling of Squanto's escape and adventures in England and beyond. A miraculous return to the land of his boyhood drew back the curtain on that tall red man's talent. Squanto's mastery of the English tongue was not so mysterious after all.

He died long before my own clear memories begin, but Mother made sure I knew that we would not have survived without the

5

kindness of Tisquantum and his native chief. Eighteen years after our 1620 arrival, head sachem Massasoit maintained peace for all fellow Wampanoags. This, while Pequots burned nearby, at the hands of Englishmen from the Connecticut valley and from near Boston. A ghastly 1637 massacre.

Luna, dearest mother, her loving life soon complete, would choose a peaceful passing. On that bright Sunday morning in August of 1638, we had left the Alden home in Duxburrow, which Mother and I called Duxbury, knowing no more than one would return. I recall clear conversation, in words that came naturally to Luna and me, as we paddled our small boat to the island of my birth.

As a little girl, I had always wondered about this dialect only Mother and I spoke. Words varied from others in Plymouth, yet left our meaning easily understood. When I got to asking, "Why these many differences?" Mother was ready with her reply. "You must speak a language, Joy, easy on the ears four centuries hence, in preparation for delivery of a 2020 message."

After nearly eighteen years of stories told me by Luna, on this very day she would complete her tales. Then I must choose to go forward in time to fully witness, or to stay in Duxbury and marry my young suitor. Would I brave a seventeenth-century life of matrimony, like Priscilla Mullins with devoted John Alden? Like all Warren sisters, with five fine Plymouth Colony husbands? Birth babies with a Governor, like Mary Collier with sour old Thomas Prence?

Or will a far distant future beckon to me? Would it really tempt? Mother warned of shocked responses from pickled old men hence. Of time-worn systems of government desperately searching for defense. Many an age would pass with only men in charge.

"Yet progress will be forged," she promised. "Seeds of democracy have been sown by that solemn *Mayflower* compact." "Tell me more," I eagerly asked when offered such enticing bits.

"True democracy stays long out of reach, until your message is heard, until truth is understood." So Luna foretold.

And there I was, during a midday pause, enjoying the warmth of Pulpit Rock beneath me, when a flash of white presented piercing golden eyes above pointed yellow beak. My visitor, with gleaming gaze, settled close to me on the burnished surface of tan stone. It was the seagull who had stayed near me as long as I could remember. Others called him Joy's shadow. "By day's end," Mother had said, "as soon as I am gone, you will have the power to fly faster than a bird, through air and through time."

In that moment, I pondered how I might choose. When mother was no longer here, could I reject my suitor's proposal? Should I be brave, knowing that "Shadow Seagull will go with you, so you need not fear. He will console you in times of need. He will protect you from harm"? Further words of comfort from Luna sounded once more in my ears. "He will need you, as much as you need him."

It is mid-August once more, the year 2019. Sixteen of you gather with me in the early morning, here at Pulpit Rock. Over four centuries of time each of you women has joined a mission to closely witness the lives of females, stories missing from most male chronicles of American history. We have seen how things went. We have determined what should come next. We must raise our voices.

Through countless lifetimes, we have traveled at the speed of light, then slowed as each of you lay dying. "It gets better," I called. "I want to see," you each replied. "Come with," I responded, and you rose up to bear witness with me.

As Shadow and I paused to be joined by you whose tales, as told to me by Mother, had pulled taut the strings of my heart, I was empowered by each of your arrivals. I felt each time more complete. Your lives have inspired, ensuring my mission dedication.

With such love and caring, as we moved forward together through time, my faith has soared. Yes, we can count on women and men of the future to join in! They need only hear from you, you who have made my choice possible. We gather again, to hear each story told, and for our final recounting of these tales of old.

Let Anne be first, then Elizabeth, Rebecca, Mary. These our first-hundred-year sounders. Next Phillis, then Jane, plus Abigail, Sally. Brave second-string followers. Then Lucy, Louisa, tales of Victoria, Dorothea. They bench our third round. Leaving Laura, Sarah, Margaret and Cid. A fourth forum founded. For climax, we offer our answers.

What does the world want?
What is it we lack?
What key opens doors,
to bring sanity back?

'Tis simple, in truth,
it's not about sinning.
It is time to go back,
to honest beginnings.

CHAPTER 1

Anne

Anne Hutchinson (1591–1643) born Marbury

OUR LEADER, JOY, HUMBLY CREDITS her mother, Luna, with deeply cherished guidance. Yet it is you, dear Joy, who gathered us over centuries and has summoned us for decades to Clark's Island, for our annual gatherings. Here, where the story of American immigrants first sprang to life, we have communed now forty-nine times.

Your 1620 birth, to an other-worldly woman who just the night before came to the aid of a brazen brotherhood of British invaders, took place in these island woods. By age eighteen you had chosen, on this same sacred spot, to accept the challenge of your mother's vision. Your choice led to this treasured sisterhood of time travelers.

Each of us first met Luna's daughter on our day of mortal passing, at afterlife's welcoming door. For me, it was a somnolent summer morning in 1643, filled with clear air, sunlight, and soft breezes, much like this August moment in 2019. Granted, it was a gruesome end to this female's time on earth. Yet what a blessing, our gifted communal travel, over four centuries forward. Strong and fascinating women on a mission, side by side.

In 1970 we met Cid, the last to join our congress of ladies. From 1971 forward, we sixteen have savored yearly assemblage at this place of unsurpassed beauty. Again today we reminisce and review, taking stock of our lives and those of others we have witnessed through time. Once more, I take my turn.

A moment near my own beginning, you sometimes ask. Joy will remember, too, when she and Shadow revisited with me far across the ocean, in an English village surrounded by green countryside. To this day, mustard blooms turn vast fields there into glorious carpets of gold. In 1591 near Alford, I was born the child of Deacon Francis Marbury, Church of England, and of a mother nee Bridget Dryden.

But future readers of these chronicles, you men and women of the twenty-first century, can find all that information on contraptions called smart phones, at a site called Wikipedia. All sixteen of us, but one, are memorialized there. Thirteen are each feted as a person in her own right. You must search the husbands of Elizabeth and Lucy to find mention of those two females who are listed only as wives. Why no entry for Sarah? Her choice not to marry provides part of an answer, about which more shall follow.

As for my early times, I recall a moment of welcome warmth in August, when perhaps seven years of age. In those days, for girls to read was largely unheard of.

Yet there I was, your fellow traveler Anne, poring over a book. Not just any book, given the times, but a 1590s printing of the Holy Bible. I already knew it nearly backwards and forwards. Triangles of glass in the window at my side transmitted bright rays of sun to light words of eternal comfort. "The Lord is my shepherd."

Joy, Shadow and I witness from the future, as again I hear my mother's voice calling. Time to rise, mark a page, and join in the garden. In side-yard learning, I harvest herbs and absorb my lesson. Mistress Bridget Marbury plumbs deep knowledge for hardy body and healthy mind. Her presence is sought daily as she is nurse and midwife for this village.

My girlhood tutelage ends abruptly, with muffled pounding and calling, causing a rush to our front door. Clatter silenced, our servant points to a tiny, near breathless neighbor boy. "Tis time, Mother says to tell you. Quick, please, she needs you now." A common plea, as Marbury home life nears year 1600. I feel, again, a soft squeeze to my shoulder, before my mother heads on her way. The anxious towhead trundles after, back to his quivering mum's bedside. He has done his duty by bringing the local sage to guide.

A moment near the middle, you enquire. That would have to be *Good Newes from New England*, as I was always a voracious reader. A man by the name of Winslow offered such enticing images from afar. In our quotidian English world, I had watched Mother's belly grow, season after season, bringing her sons and daughters to a total of fifteen. My first sister Bridget, my first brother Anthony, and Elizabeth had gone to their graves, the former two already replaced with namesakes.

My own wedding was well behind me by 1624, that year of *Good Newes*. My first child Edward, now eleven years of age, had arrived soon after my littlest sister, Katherine. My mum was at my side each time my husband and I brought new life into this world. Now I had nine, on track to near Mother's total of fifteen, before William Hutchinson and I, ten years beyond publication of Winslow's tease, would hazard a voyage to hallowed New England.

A most terrifying moment, far more than months at sea with baby Susannah in my arms, comes three years beyond our 1634 crossing. The end of my first trial nears. "What have I done?" I ask myself, the only woman in the room where I face my inquisitors. True, I have dared to think for myself, to speak for myself, and encouraged others to do the same. At first some women had gathered with me, to listen and speak their own thoughts. "How dare they!" others had scolded.

Then a scattering of men joined us at my home in Boston, after the Sunday gatherings led by revered ministers of the town and other male preachers in our colony named after the Massachusetts native tribe.

Our mixed-gender meetings increased the ire of Governor Winthrop, who fumed in his fine residence across the way.

"She knows not her place as a woman," those holier-than-thou men sputter. Now I await their conclusion on this judgment day. A strongly reasoned defense of my actions may have done more harm than good to my case. "You are unfit to remain in our midst," they conclude. "Banishment," I hear.

They were not done with me yet. In a second trial, the church must have "her" say. The same male ministers and magistrates of Massachusetts Colony agree once more to reject my belief in a woman's right to use her own mind to determine her own faith. "Heresy," I am told, and "excommunication" is my fate.

As I exit into the wintry afternoon, young Mary Dyer comes to squeeze my hand, bravely walking with me through the gauntlet of masculine fury. Even in this afterlife, I shall never forget that moment in 1638, or the comforting feel of Mary's hand in mine.

There are many wonderful and inspired moments at my adopted home in Rhode Island, where kind-hearted Roger Williams welcomes us warmly. But my husband has reached end of days, a mere four years after our Portsmouth arrival. His passing, and word that Massachusetts Colony may try to draw Rhode Island into its fold, has left me uncertain of my safety, and that of my many children. My Boston-born cherub, Zuriel, is a mere child of six years. New Amsterdam, known for religious tolerance, becomes my destination, far from treacherous New England shores.

There, on a warm day in August 1643, just a year and a few months into our stay in what has become known as the Bronx, I meet Shadow Seagull and our fellow witness, Joy Franklin. Her entrancing blue eyes peer into my face, as I feel mortal life slip away. My own last glance is toward the meadow where boulders have provided a playground of sorts, for my youngest girls Susannah and Zuriel.

Natives, leaving me and six children at death's door, snatch up Susannah. Sunlight streams through towering trees beyond the

12

clearing. My daughter's autumn gold hair shines. My executioners disappear with her, into the woods.

Joy tells me, "It gets better." "I want to see," I reply, to which she responds, "Come with." It is Susannah I most want to see, if that should prove possible.

Before, betwixt and beyond the arrivals of each of you fellow travelers, I recall other events, as we slowed to observe. Forty miles to the north of Plymouth, Governor Winthrop, still fuming at my female audacity, hears news of my massacre at the hands of Indians. As he gloats in Boston, Joy, Shadow, and I witness the man's willful ignorance of sad realities. The natives, for many a good reason, had lost patience with Dutch intruders.

Those wielding tomahawks saw me as one of the nasty Netherlanders. This was not of note to my Massachusetts persecutor. Winthrop saw my death as the hand of the Lord, doing justice as the Governor saw it. According to God, Master John Winthrop firmly believed, terrible wrath was due female challengers, unmindful of their place in this world.

I next see Mary Dyer, in the year 1660, when a Governor Endicott rules that same fair city upon a hill. She, my fellow believer in her own inner light, answers him, "I speak the words the Lord speaks to me." This Quaker woman's challenge is all he needs to proclaim her punishment: death by hanging. Many in Boston come to gawk. Joy, Shadow, and I sadly bear witness, as Mary's feet dangle in the wind.

Many times over, we come upon like fury in the face of a female who does not back down, who claims status equal to males, who thinks for herself. It is not only men defending their male prerogative. Women, too, will fight for that status quo, pitting themselves against their own sex.

And, each time I retell my story, I wonder how it might have ended, were it not only men in charge. Granted, there have been, and will be, the men who sometimes come to the defense of a female's rights. Elizabeth can speak to that, when her turn comes.

Yet our travels together through time have revealed the stranglehold of male supremacy, far down the road. Long after my daughter Susannah was returned by the natives who plucked her away, we saw her raise a family with John Cole of Boston, yielding a great-grandson, many times over, by the name of Mitt Romney. My descendant, our time traveling group could sadly see, seemed to relish a 2016 supporting role, as the world blocked a woman's aspirations to be United States' Commander in Chief.

"What does she really believe?" we heard Mitt say. "I think people wonder, can they really trust Hillary Clinton?" Other dismissive remarks by my own flesh and blood, who like Winthrop had served as a Governor of the land where the Massachusetts tribe once thrived, reignited a fire in the phantom of a body I once had, left to bleed life away so long ago, in the Bronx.

America had not heard the last of Hillary Clinton. In 2008, a fellow named Barrack Obama won the prize of the Presidency. He then chose his finest opponent, Hillary Clinton, as his Secretary of State. Pride in America was high, and dignity reigned for nearly a decade.

The rest of that story must wait. We have Elizabeth, and fourteen more, to hear speak today. But first, another pleasure awaits. Let us listen, once more, to Joy.

JOY 2

WHEN SHADOW JOINED ME DURING that August 1638 midday pause of which I spoke earlier on this 2019 sojourn, I could not resist a test flight of the sort Mother had promised. "Welcome," I called to the gull and cried out, "Let's go!" To my delight, my feathered friend understood without delay. We rose in unison from the boulder, circling higher and higher until land and sea receded below.

All became a real-life version of maps I'd seen rendered by the menfolk of Plymouth Colony. Gorgeous greens and blues swirled below, with wondrous shades of white and gray at our shoulders, until we slowed and then steadied to look back from our perch near the clouds.

From this bird's-eye view, I could see the bed of pine boughs Mother and I had arranged during the dew-fresh hours of the morning. Ears had perked in those woods; a doe and her fawn had watched as Luna, resting on the cushion of branches, murmured the beginnings of her day's long tale. "To fulfill your purpose, should you choose," she had said to me, "you must live four hundred years."

"So, I, too, will die? In 2020?" I queried. "We shall see," was Mother's reply. "They may wish to kill the messenger." She then continued her admonitions. "Four centuries from your birth, our kinfolk will need guidance as they reach a fork in the road. Your message can be informed by all that you witness. Now, before my day's end departure, I must complete my story of all that will be."

While I hovered above the island with Shadow in 1638, I recalled more of Luna's early morning words. "Tell me all," I had begged. "Tell me again, dear Mother, of my own beginnings on Clark's Island!"

"Here is where I came to lie, in the wee hours of the day you were born," the retelling began. "The men had given thanks to the Lord that all their lives were spared in that dreadful storm, two nights prior. With the mast in three pieces and the sail floundering on raging waves, somehow a last desperate effort by those at the oars had brought them from churning seas into quiet waters. Grace, delivered by God, guided them to this peaceful lee side of the one glorious isle in a dark, stormy bay. So the men chose to believe."

"Did they know you were there, too?" I asked, fully aware of the answer, but eager to hear my mother's voice tell me once more.

"No, the men had no idea of other forces at play. The mystery of a woman's power to will herself where she is needed, and to guide with a gentle hand and glowing light, was simply not on their minds."

Again that morning, Mother told me of young John Alden, and near sixty men more, back on the *Mayflower* with the women. Governor Carver's wife was among them and she was Luna's mistress. Other Carver servants brought the total to six. That embarrassment of riches might explain the number assigned by Will Bradford years later in his tales of their travels across the Atlantic to New England: five servants only in Carver's cadre. My mother was the secret sixth.

"And there you were, my child, rolled up in a ball in my belly, a circle within a circle, nearly ready to emerge. I knew it was your fate to be born on an island in a bay, to which I must transport myself quickly. And I knew there was another matter of great import, as I sensed the distress call coming from that spot. Rising in the stormy mist, leaving ship and occupants behind, I made my magic flight. Finding Master Carver and the others struggling to survive was my mission in those moments."

It has been called Clark's Island since that fateful night. Over the years, Mother had told me the male version of events, crediting sailor

Coppin with calling out, having heard a "sound" ahead, and captain's mate John Clarke with steady seamanship and the honor of stepping first ashore. All true, to which Luna always adds, "It was I, with you along for the ride, dear Joy, shining my light and sending cries of encouragement. It was I who could see and show the way to the island shores." There was never pride or triumph in her voice in the telling. This was the simple truth of the matter, that the desperate men had needed her help to survive.

My mother's hair was of a mysterious color, blonde yet with such silvery tone it reminded me of moonlight rather than sun rays. My hair is blonde of the more golden sort. Luna's eyes were of a graphite gray, ringing lighter gray tones with dapples of near white. Mine are blue of the kind Luna called entrancing.

"Right from birth," my mother would say, "you have been a beautiful child." Followed by, "Always remember, beauty is as beauty does." Like all children of *Mayflower* passengers, and like later arrivals on ships such as the *Fortune,* the *Anne*, and the *Little James*, I had to do whatever possible to help. We littlest ones toddled with chamber pots from indoor shelter to side yard, providing sustenance for corn stalks embraced by beautiful leaves of green.

Mistress and Master Carver died the first winter. The ship *Anne* arrived in 1623 and carried Master Warren's wife, Elizabeth, and their five daughters. It was their family with whom Luna and I lived. They were the ones we helped, first and foremost, as two more births brought Warren sons into our world: Nathaniel in 1624 and Joseph in 1627.

When I was seven, it was my favorite chore to tend to three-year-old Nathaniel while Mistress Warren nurtured the newest baby, Joe. We two youngsters often climbed the hill to view the harbor below, keeping an eager eye on the horizon for any hint of a newly arriving vessel. We played by the brook where one afternoon, Nathaniel nearly went to his maker.

I had wandered uphill picking berries. Returning leisurely by the brook, I heard a curious sound, a muted splashing. Horrified to see my little charge had fallen in and was flailing, I grabbed a handy branch to extend. After rescuing him, I held little Nathaniel close and offered the Goddess of Good silent thanks that I had not lost my precious young friend, nor failed in my duties.

It was Master Warren who met his maker in 1628, leaving Widow Warren the only woman in Plymouth to remain in possession of her own property. And so it continued, until her death some forty-odd years later. The story must wait, but her ownership would not go without challenge.

By 1633, Mother and I had transitioned from the southern Warren family lands toward the northern outskirts of Plymouth Colony. This was where the Alden and Standish families had settled in Duxburrow. Some claimed that name for the town carved from Plymouth Colony land was chosen in honor of our military leader's ancestral home far across the Atlantic. The greatest excitement that year came when whole families, such as the Colliers, arrived together on the *Mary & Jane*. Master Collier's daughters, Sarah, Rebecca, Mary, and Elizabeth, would marry sons of Brewster, Cole, Prence, and Southworth, all in short order.

The first two nuptials came within a year's time, in 1634. Then, in 1635, Mary wed the widowed Governor, Thomas Prence. There was a year's pause, as a stepson of past and future Governor Bradford, Constant Southworth, did his courting. Then Constant wed bride Elizabeth Collier. That was in 1637, the year before my mother made her exit. Bellies grew in girth; more and more babies were born.

"Mischief will come of another Collier girl's match," Mother told me in confidence, for she always had that power to portend. "Older sister Jane stayed in England, but her daughter Sarah Walker will one day brave the Atlantic, and then marry Nathaniel Warren, your favorite little charge other than Ruth Alden."

I often did not understand Luna's full meaning, but knew all would become clear in the centuries to come. I did know that the Collier girls' father, William, was a wealthy man, a financier of the *Mayflower* travelers. His holdings in Duxbury (as you ladies, Luna, and I call it) were of great value. Might money be at the root of some evil? Time would tell.

Matrimonial prospects for me, should I *not* choose living and witnessing four hundred years, entertained my young mind. Constant's brother, Thomas Southworth, was a fine looking fellow, in his own way. I am not one to kiss and tell, but as a girl, I had my own hormones speaking to me. I allowed myself to respond at times, in certain ways, yet with caution. And I shall remain cautious about what I say, for a girl's reputation is another matter of value.

The Collier girls' heritage had clearly served them in order to marry well. Young women had few other options towards which they might strive, as Mother would observe to me throughout my girlhood. Thomas Southworth might find himself entranced by my blue eyes and golden locks, treasure the fullness of my lips, but how might he feel about the value of my ancestry, or apparent lack thereof?

Mother and I were servants then, at the Duxbury home of the Aldens, where no one knew or spoke of my paternal heritage. There, my favorite duty was minding four-year-old Ruth Alden. Mistress Alden tended to endless chores and supervised five older children, while her belly swelled in anticipation of number seven.

As a baby, I was one of just fifty survivors of the winter of my birth. Almost eighteen years later, I was surrounded by nearly four hundred souls in Plymouth Colony. There were other boys, beyond Thomas, who tried to catch my eye, exchange a word or two, or perhaps meet up while walking the Duxburrow Trail. There was only one of whom I shall not speak, nor tell of what happened, save to say I was robbed of choice in terrifying moments seared forever in my brain.

We travelers have seen how the world today allows some men to do grievous harm, yet still rise to positions of ultimate power. Four centuries after my own days walking the trails of the New World, the words of Christine Blasey Ford will not be believed. Men in power are determined to rule supreme in the halls of government and discount the female and her plight. I, too, knew when it happened to me, to stay silent in the face of a world where men had all the say. I knew not to tell.

Mother told me that both of my favorite charges -- the Warrens' son, Nathaniel, and the Aldens' daughter, Ruth -- have important roles to play in the centuries to come. My special role, unlike theirs, Luna said, may not involve a marriage or resulting offspring. My mission began with the union of Luna and my father, as many years back as the years of my life so far and nine months more. That story, which took place far across the seas in the Dutch countryside, Mother promised to detail, for my ears only, on the day of her passing.

But now, in this moment of recounting here by Pulpit Rock, it is time for our second story, the tale of Elizabeth Warren. On the day of her passing in 1673, I met up with Mistress Warren again, along with my feathered friend Shadow, and Anne, our sole fellow traveler. Joined by Elizabeth, we move onward to witness evolving female lives in America.

CHAPTER 2

Elizabeth

Elizabeth Warren (1583–1673) born Walker

TRAVERSING HUNDREDS OF YEARS TOGETHER, pausing at these annual events to converse at length, our speech has become a shared tongue, the language of Joy. Our passings have rendered us each mere remnants of molecules, dancing in the light. Our hue, best perceived by mortals with closed eyes, is mostly shared in a range from gold to silver. Yet our different personalities live on in occasional, small bright flashes of color. A mortal observer at Pulpit Rock might notice, when Anne speaks, a hint of crimson. Joy says she does.

Umber, it seems, flashes at times when it is my turn to recount, offering hints of a life lived off the main stage and behind the scenes, close to the earth. In the sixteen hundreds, my Warren descendants were to become holders of property ranging from Hobbs Hole in Plymouth, all the way south to Sandwich, where the land known as Cape Cod begins her reach of arm into the Atlantic. It was my job to remain a force of nature, emerging from the shadows only at imperative moments.

At these gatherings when I tell of memories, my most ancient are, like those of Anne, set in an English village. As I have proffered more than once, an indelible moment came while dockside, amidst a bustle of passengers bristling with anxieties in anticipation of a daring ocean voyage. I am easily transported back to that *Mayflower* boarding day.

Many, like my husband, maintain a calm front. Some fail, erupting in cries of distress. As departure looms, it is easy to second-guess the choice to go to sea. While Richard remains confident and resolute, I see that it is the fears of our five daughters that most threaten his composure. With great effort, I manage to smile, offering assurance to our girls.

We are strangers to those calling themselves saints, their beliefs inspiring a hazardous voyage. Such profound faith in our English King's God seems wise to match. "The Lord will see your father through," I tell Mary, Anna, Sarah, Elizabeth, and Abigail.

It was an advantageous choice, time would tell, me staying behind with young daughters and managing the family business. In those days, a woman could not trade unless no man of the family was present to do so. My husband's departure allowed me that task, within the confines of English law. So, the year 1620 saw the ship *Mayflower* set sail, beginning our three-year family separation.

The girls and I arrived in Plymouth in 1623. The Warren clan has since expanded beyond our imagination in that moment of time. Today, in 2019, over thirty million living souls are said to descend from those who, like my husband, crossed over on the *Mayflower*. It has been claimed that nearly a quarter of that number may be Warren descendants.

Disembarking the vessel *Anne*, reunion desires drove me directly to Richard's welcoming arms. We two shared precious moments of connubial bliss. Our boy Nathaniel came first into that New World, in 1624. The birth of our seventh and last child, Joseph, came in 1627.

My Richard, his days sadly numbered, bid farewell the following year. Life came to mirror those three years in England, when without a male presence I could act as if I were a person in my own right. Would

I ever remarry? I thought not, thank you. Let the mirror expand, into four-and-a-half decades as a self-sufficient widow.

It was our daughters and sons who were destined to brave the world of matrimony. Joy has made mention of a Collier girl's daughter, Sarah Walker. I was well pleased, seeing my first-born son, Nathaniel, settle down in 1645 with lovely Sarah, of Duxburrow's William Collier line.

My girls had long prior gained dowries of various plots of land on which grandchildren, with the last names of Bartlett, Little, Cooke, Church, and Snow, could grow in some comfort. Nathaniel gained his land, as well, with his marriage to Goodwife Sarah Warren. So, too, would Joseph and his betrothed Prissy Faunce, in due time.

My eldest son's grandmother-in-law, Jane Collier, had ideas of her own on this landowner score. As wife of Master Collier, the wealthiest man in Duxbury, she seemed to believe her own descendants in the Warren family were due more than the offspring of my daughters. Mistress Collier was a fine example of a woman happy to see men in charge, as long as it was of great benefit to her, and to those in her line of descent.

We were not once but twice in the court room, in order for my advocate Bradford and the appointed panel to reach a conclusion that would see no further challenge. The William Collier family was not pleased with the results of those court proceedings. They were disappointed that the panel ruled for Mistress Warren who, "shall enjoy all the rest of her lands and all of them to whom she hath already at any time heretofore disposed any part thereof by gift, sale or otherwise, or shall hereafter do the same, to them and their heirs forever without any trouble or molestation."

My son could see the legal matter laid to rest by 1652. He then lived out a fine final fifteen years, but not without residual effect. It was my youngest, Joseph, with whom I would reside. And troubles of another sort came after my Nathaniel's 1667 trip to the grave.

My namesake grandchild, Elizabeth Warren, sixth in Nathaniel and Sarah's brood of twelve, was just thirteen when her father died. As my own passing neared in 1673, I could feel an impact on her life and sense her woes in matters of love and male entitlement.

The Doty boy, Joseph, had a reputation. No real need for connubial blessings for carnal pleasures. It was plain for me to see that he had an eye on my dear, vulnerable young Elizabeth. I feared that my grandchild might throw caution to the wind, that she might not heed my warnings. Or might fall prey to a male determined to have his way. Should I speak up more clearly? What if a burgeoning belly should bring shame heaped on my girl, far beyond any for the boy who made his conquest?

Joy came to me, in my final moments, with assurances that, "It will get better," and that my worries about my offspring, granddaughter Elizabeth first and foremost, would ultimately be laid to rest. "I want to see," I said. "Come with," Joy replied. So here I am, with her, with Shadow Seagull, and with all of you like-minded spirits of the afterlife.

A mere few years beyond my own passing, treatment of natives by men in charge yielded a most terrible conflict. King Phillip's War, they called it. For decades after the gory climax, his head rotted on a pole in Plymouth for all to see. Joy, Shadow, Anne, and I bore solemn witness, and then looked about for solace. I got to see that my grandchild, Elizabeth, though never married to the Doty father of her first child, did find a husband in William Greene.

Centuries later, we all had the thrill of witnessing another Doty progeny join in championing the cause of women. There was Elias Doty, at the same spot as our Mary Folger's many times great-granddaughter Lucretia Mott, holding court at Seneca Falls in New York State. They declared the independence of females, in 1848. It was worth a try, I say today. Mrs. Mott, along with her young protégé Susan Anthony and scores more, was demanding to be heard, in ways I would never have risked in my own era, two hundred years prior.

Joining them was Joseph Doty's brother Isaac's offspring, many generations down. And how sweet to see that Elias, in the 1800s, was married to a many times great-granddaughter of the only baby born at sea during the *Mayflower* voyage. Joy knows that story well through her mother's repeated accounts. Peregrine White lived to father seven sons. It was son Daniel whose line led to Susan Russell White, co-signer, with her Doty husband, Elias, of the Declaration of Sentiments at Seneca Falls.

More than eighty years after that bold feminine stance, with Lucretia half a century gone to her grave, I saw Amelia, a product, many generations down the line, of my daughter Anna's marriage to Ephraim Little, cross the same Atlantic I had braved with my girls in 1623. Heading in the opposite direction, over three hundred years later, Amelia flew like a bird, Newfoundland to Ireland. Done in an invention called an airplane, fueled by a substance called gasoline.

What courage that took. What determination. Eleven of us now deceased females could easily join alongside to share in that 1923 feminine triumph. Five had yet to join our gaggle. Earthbound Dorothea could read the New York papers, trumpeting the full import of my six times great-granddaughter's brash disregard for life and limb. So too, Laura, Sarah, Margaret, and Cid have all said they recall where they were, when hearing such thrilling Amelia Earhart news.

I've come to think aviator Amelia's insistence on freedom in her marriage before finally agreeing to wed was her most courageous choice of all. I recall my granddaughter Elizabeth's troubles with men in a world of masculine systems. How might things have gone for my namesake, if it had not been only men in charge?

Our first speaker, Anne, made note of men who, at times, come to the defense of a female's rights. It was Bradford to whom she knew I could and would give warm thanks. To him I owe credit for my unique status. No other woman in Plymouth Colony had full charge of her own landholdings, as I did for more than forty years. That he let me do.

At what cost to me? I had no choice but to prove to others, and nearly convince myself along the way, that I, too, believed in supremacy of males. "She was honorably buried on the 24th of October 1673," was entered into records of the colony. There was no precedent for such mention of deceased females. But I had successfully bowed to God and the men of this land, who so closely resembled Him. The records also emphasized, "Mistress Elizabeth Warren, an aged widow, having lived a godly life, came to her grave as a shock of corn fully ripe."

Some natives also chose to mimic English forms of worship, to adopt our imported godly ways. Metacom, Joy has said, chose for himself the name Phillip. But when all was said and done, the war bearing his name wiped out most of the Wampanoag tribes. My own grandson, it must be said, saw personally to the wiping out of that Indian leader. King Phillip's demise came at the hand of Benjamin Church, son of Elizabeth, my fourth daughter of five.

The men had left England behind, to start anew in this land, free to worship as they saw fit. But this did not mean freedom of choice, of any substantive sort, for their women, nor real choice for natives. The white men were in charge here, in the eyes of both church and state. Leaders of the day carefully kept those like-minded institutions wedded in tight support of one another.

My unusual status was, all could see, an exception to their rules. That was a mere baby step, allowing me wings to fly, while other women of the day trudged along behind their men. Through the centuries, other females have risen above the masses, achieving some footnote in history. Yet, more often than not, the coattails of a husband swept her into that limelight. A man's passing, or absence of some kind, might leave her to fill his shoes, in one way or another.

I am thinking of another great-granddaughter, many times over, and of the Brooklyn Bridge. When Washington Roebling, in charge of the project in 1883, could not rise from his bed, my plucky descendant, Emily Warren, stepped in to save the day.

Her husband lay victim to Caisson's disease. Rising to the challenge, Emily filled his position as Chief Engineer, deftly managing completion of that great monument to civilization. The world celebrated man's achievement, with a nod to the woman who saw it through to the end. We fellow travelers paused to savor that moment in time, too. Through chance circumstances, in small ways, things had gotten better.

But a most critical step was, and is, yet left undone. No part of the U.S. Constitution codifies equal, fifty-fifty percent representation, to our fifty percent female part of American citizenry. Thus, our freedom is yet to come. Our travels with Joy aim to shed light on this very conundrum. So, now, once again, we are due to hear from fellow voyager Rebecca.

I yield the floor back to Joy, who so carefully guides us along that path.

JOY 3

"WHY ARE MY EYES BLUE, and your eyes gray?" As a child, I wondered about things of all kinds, and peppered Luna with questions of this sort.

My eyes have a graphite blue circle at the border, ringing sky blue with a hint of gray. This seemed of great interest to Thomas Southworth. Luna's eyes, as I have said, were gray, conjuring for me the portentous beauty of silvery storm clouds. The hue of my father's eyes remained unknown to any but my mother.

On the final day of Luna's life in August 1638, I learned more than the bare details she had shared to date. More than the last name Franklin. More than implied nuptials in Leyden. I learned that his eyes were blue, nearly just like mine.

This may seem a small bit of knowledge to some. Yet for me, and for many as I have seen in my travels, the eyes are windows to the soul. Shadow's eyes have a golden gleam, bringing warm comfort to me, much like the soft stroking of his head on my shoulder when he sees me in distress. We have needed to soothe one another, in ways like this, throughout our centuries of witness.

When I had not yet chosen to make my long journey, it was green eyes which nearly lured me from my mission. And Thomas Southworth's touch. His lips on my cheek. It was forbidden to explore this physical realm in real depth, but youngsters like us found our ways to test the waters.

Later in the morning of my first joint flight with Shadow, I returned to the island forest where Luna resumed her reminiscences. There was so much more of a chronicle than I had ever heard. I learned details of my Dutch mother and English father, with new images from their meeting in Holland, before the *Speedwell* and *Mayflower* set sail for a New World. All this has become part of my memories, melding with ecstatic sensations on my time travels with Shadow.

Mother seemed free of her usual modest restraint when she told me of my conception in a wooded setting, far across the sea. Many had traveled to the Netherlands for freedom to worship as they saw fit. It is as if I am right there with her.

In the lowlands of the Dutch countryside, a charming blue-eyed visitor from across the Channel caught the eye of a nineteen-year-old girl with silvery blonde hair. He had a way with words and a gentle touch, bringing wonderfully warm sensations as his hand pressed lightly on the small of Luna's back. That a sweet, prolonged meeting of lips could yield such pleasure so far afield in her body, amazed and thrilled her.

Press of bodies brings proof of passion. Not a thought was given to convention and hours were spent in the verdant woods nearby.

It was then, in the very moment I was conceived, that visions first came to Luna. Her child would be a girl. She would have a purpose of immeasurable import. There would be travel to a place far away, to bear fruit many centuries down the road. Before the eyes of this lass newly with child, passed detailed images of all that was to come. The centuries became known to her, and to her alone. So my mother said. What to do with this knowledge? Time would tell.

Among Luna's tales that August day in 1638 was the story of Rebecca. But, no! I am not yet ready to cede my time to our next fellow time traveler. First there are other questions I recall posing for Luna.

"Why are only the men in charge, making all the rules?" Throughout my girlhood, I presented my mother with this query many times over. Luna told me tale after tale of men in charge for centuries to come, making choices for women. To my young girl's mind, the results ranged from horrifying to barely satisfactory, with many a hint of distastefulness. Anne's story conjured crimson, with inspiration hounded by dreadful shock. Elizabeth's life saga, in soothing umber tone, reassured me to some degree. My own memory of choice stripped away one dark day on the Duxbury Trail rose anew to haunt my heart once again.

Rebecca and Mary repeat a pattern, each time I hear them speak. Men chose to strip Goody Nurse of far more than choice. Her very life was cruelly and deliberately snatched away. The amber aura conjured by repetition of Rebecca's tale leaves me each time deeper in dread for our world. Then, comforting cobalt dances in my view, as Mary proudly speaks her truth. Slowly, measured confidence rises to attest that "It gets better."

Yet even the best of endings has always left a slightly bitter tang behind. "That is how it is for now, Joy," Luna replied more than once, when I repeated my lament, "Why are only men in charge?"

"This ice age may seem long, yet will be followed by rebirth, in due time." Even now, I cling to heartwarming words from my mother in centuries past. "You see, my dear Joy, women number half the population. You shall witness, my child, a rightful claim to half the governing power. One day, rest assured, women and men will be in charge, in equal numbers."

It would clearly be a long wait. Mother soothed, each evening bedtime hour, with a prayer just our own. No other ears must hear our blasphemous nighttime ode.

"To the goddess and god of good, I say
I did my best to be good today.
To be kind to others as best I could,
to be kind to myself as I know I should.
Now I will take the time to rest,
then tomorrow when I rise refreshed,
again I shall strive to do my best."

When the sun rose to light the marsh grasses of Eagle Tree Pond, Luna urged, "Enjoy your time with Ruth, sweet child." So I headed many times over for the inlets of Bluefish River with the youngest daughter of Mistress Alden in tow. There we played in the muddy flats at low tide, returning with browned feet and skirts to the pond to rinse away that day's signs of earthly delights.

We were tasked with keeping an eye for a bubble or a sometimes-startling squirt, telling of mussels and clams hiding from our eager hands. There was pleasure in having mealtime treasures piled high in our basket, ready to add to a noontime or evening repast. Most of all, with Mother's blessing, we savored each chance to write at will, with a small stick in the mud. Ruth wrote her letters, I wrote my tracts, such as my mother's secret prayer from the night before. Songbirds entertained us, while gulls like Shadow circled, then landed nearby.

My mind returns to a favorite moment in the marshes, looking up from a muddy floor, with the warm wet feel of earth between my toes. A great green crown of towering elm above, flanked by elegant blue sky, graced my eye, as a light, salty ocean breeze from the east gently cooled my brow. To the west, a wondrous white bank of clouds had parted at center, opening itself to giant rays of light reaching down to greet me and my tiny companion. Ruth, also, paused in her play. We two gazed in awe at the glorious sight.

"Is that the goddess of good?" my mind queried, though I dared not utter such a thought aloud. "Is she looking down on us now?" As if he read my thought, Shadow Seagull glided in to settle on my shoulder, with a shriek of delight.

"All the goodness that lies in we girls and all the goodness in the boys, is reflected in the great natural beauty around us." Those were the words I dared to say to my little charge. "Letters are the tools we need to form the words to express our wonder at the glory of this world."

Back at the Alden home, the master of the house read aloud from the Bible each evening, encouraging his young ones, sisters along with brothers, to become versed in such knowledge. Yet the boys were granted extra time for honing their writing skills. The namesake eldest son would be served well by his ability to put a story of his own to parchment.

I find this memory serves as a reminder that I have taken too many moments for my own tale, leaving us overdue to hear from that third fellow female on our journey through time.

Pray speak to us, dear Rebecca.

CHAPTER 3

Rebecca

Rebecca Nurse (1621–1692) born Towne

WHAT IS THIS AMBER, OUR Joy sees? Fossilized resin, born of conifer trees from home and abroad, then washed up by the sea. Or buried in land, just like me. Red, yellow, and orange – they rust to a joyful mix, making autumn gold. Hardened beauty strengthened by aging.

I was hanged in the Spring. My sister Mary Easty was hanged in the Fall. The color amber formed a blessed beauty, a witness to ugly acts. In this great surround, finally, those killings ceased.

We travelers see that misogyny still lives as voices cry out, "One thing only not to like. He hasn't put that witch in jail!" A woman like me, Hillary being her name. A man like a Don, on his Mafia-like throne, hunting home and abroad. He determined to dictate, oblivious to and unheeding of the law.

Many times now, I have dutifully told my story from beginning to end, here at Pulpit Rock. I greatly appreciate, each time, this unique opportunity. Please do not misunderstand, but today, on this lovely morning in August 2019, I refuse to again commence at birth. I shall start with memories made possible for me, by Joy, just moments after an end.

But first, I shall remind my listeners. Anne spoke of her descendant Mitt, seventieth governor of Massachusetts. He was a man with no kind words for Hillary Clinton when she dared aspire to serve as America's Commander in Chief. For me, too, that boy is a great-grandson many times over. My daughter, Elizabeth Nurse, bears credit for that Mitt Romney line.

Was my daughter Elizabeth there in 1692, with Benjamin, pulling my lifeless body from the shallow grave on Gallows Hill? I know Elizabeth never brooked the question, "Can you trust Rebecca Nurse?" All heard my testimony, "I have never wished ill on anyone." My daughters and sons, my neighbors as well, had no doubt that I spoke truly.

In the 2000s, what of my great-grandson, Mitt? I know not. I can only hope. Meanwhile, I wait to see what words he speaks to all of America the next time a woman runs for the highest office in this land.

All sixteen of us joyfully bore witness, in 2001 to 2003.

A woman, a one and only, held office as Massachusetts Governor. Jane Swift brought added meaning to oft-repeated words from Joy, "It gets better." We saw Swift declare the last five of twenty victims of 1690s misogyny and greed "innocent" of those bogus witchcraft charges, brought long ago by the all-male court of Oyer and Terminer.

If only women had been among the judges, in equal numbers, sharing power in my times. Surely the madness, and the green-eyed, envious grasping for land and material things, would have been tempered by the milk of human kindness.

My own words in 1692? "I can say before my Eternal father I am innocent, and God will clear my innocency."

To evangelicals of 2019 I say, you hanged me when I believed in a white male God.

Hang me over and over again, if you like.

For I do declare, I no longer hold ancient beliefs, proscribed, in my day, by both church and state.

I claim my freedom to choose my beliefs. Give me freedom, liberty from old religion, the old masculine system, or again, if you must, give me death.

They gave me death in 1692 and denied my clearly held Christian faith. It was death by hanging, with no right to a proper burial where other "Christian" bodies lay. First Joy came to me, with Shadow, calling, "It gets better!"

"How so?" I asked.

"Come with. Come see!" I heard in reply. From my shallow grave, I rose, to bear witness in the dark of that same ghastly night. Poor Benjamin, my youngest, wept while he removed me from that grave to carry my hardening form to the waiting wagon. Then he drove me to our family homestead in Salem Village, tears still streaming down.

But, enough. I choose now to recall, with Joy and feathered friend, with Anne and Elizabeth, too, travels back to my girlhood. There ocean air spoke of salty North Sea secrets. Fishwives frightened children with tales of haunted beaches. There were greater fears for a girl of seven, as hunger weakened fellow villagers. It seemed that deaths came daily.

I am there now, as I speak. It is 1628, and baby Edmund is crying, reminding me of two other infants, years dead and gone. "Will he live?" I ask Mother.

"God willing," she murmurs.

"Joanna," Father says, "let us trust in the Lord. This time, he will not take another."

Somehow, he was right. Four years later, right again. Jacob was born in 1632, lived and grew just fine. Two more years and Mary came in 1634 and she thrived. I was thirteen then, a serious and thoughtful girl.

Church and state were one, the King and a male God, equally in charge. William and Joanna Blessing Towne, and we, their offspring, could not choose a form of worship. "Feare God, Honour the Kynge," the gold lettering on our St. Nicholas church pulpit proclaimed. The

Bishop in London told ministers what they could and couldn't say. Attendance was required. First King James, then King Charles, with God were one, together dictating all.

Across the North Sea, rebel pilgrims had come and gone. Holland was a home for that decade or more. Now survivors of a *Mayflower* voyage, with passengers who followed on ships of all kinds, peopled a land called New England. Separatists at Plymouth or Puritans around Boston braved resentments from natives. Yet they had more than one choice of church to attend. Perhaps, as well, freedom from hunger.

There was a long sea journey about my fifteenth year. Towns near Salem become safe havens for my family. There, Sarah and Joseph come into the world. Edmund married in 1652. Jacob married in 1657, as I had done in 1644. For Mary, it was 1655, if memory serves, when she took the Easty name. Sarah married in 1659 and Joseph wed in 1665.

Three girls and three boys carrying on the Towne family legacy. Two of us were to die by hanging although we were innocent as the day is long; the others to mourn through many centuries. Today, we still grieve the loss. We grieve repetition of dreams quashed.

Hillary, we grieve your loss at the hands of those who term you witch, then falsely cry "Witch Hunt" when their own dirty deeds are investigated.

It was a real witch hunt in 1692. By then, Joy's favorite charge, Ruth Alden Bass, had passed. But her brother, John Junior, a merchant in Boston, was among those caught up in the web of lies, fending off manufactured accusations believed by compromised men in charge. "I used to trust you, John Alden," a supposed friend said. "Now I am not so sure." John wrote about the "madness" in eloquent prose, once the world "came to its senses."

But it is my sister, Mary, who wrote the greatest words of all. Because of Joy, I was there to bear witness to her touching testament. Dear Mary could see that all measures to convince the heartless of her freedom from guilt had failed.

In writing she begged, "I petition not to your honours for my own life," asking only "if it be possible, no more innocent blood may be shed."

And, as can be seen to this day in her plea, my sister kindly implores Salem judges "not to deny this my humble petition from a poor dying innocent person." For should they heed her admonitions, Mary concluded, "I question not but the Lord will give a blessing to your endeavors."

We travelers, the first three to join Joy and Shadow, wept with the crowd, to see my sister Mary's feet jerk and sway, her lifeless body robbed of breath by the holier-than-thou. It was a sad contrast to the amber beauty all around us.

"No more innocent blood," we called out over and over, midst our sorrowful tears.

The mortals of Salem did not seem to hear our pleas. And after all these years, in 2019, angry voices continue to decry perceived witches. Demeaning of women lives on with no end yet to this lie. I yield my turn, with an impatient yet hopeful sigh.

Let's hear from a different Mary, a fourth fellow spirit to join our tribe. But first Joy, with welcome prelude, to she who in 1704 would arrive.

JOY 4

Priscilla Alden was admired by all for great skill at her spinning wheel. No time for hours of reading like husband John, though at times he did read aloud as she spun. Master Alden's skills at writing and numbers would lead to a lifetime of honorable civic duties in Duxbury, the sort only performed by men.

Our garden was mostly the purview of the Mistress, of Priscilla's children, and of we her servants. Cabbage, carrots, cucumbers, leeks, lettuce, parsnip, and pumpkin played a part in proudly produced results. Those were colorful accompaniments to abundant fish and shellfish in Duxbury and Plymouth Bays. Lobsters, bright red when boiled, some considered a savory treat then, as is still true today.

Southward across sea and land and on into Nantucket Sound, time would show yields of similar wealth for generations to come. When Anne, Elizabeth, Rebecca, Shadow and I would meet up with Mary, at her 1704 passing, the Folgers proved to be as blessed as the Aldens with such benefits. And for the women, there were hardships similar to those I witnessed while a girl in Duxbury.

My complaints to Luna about only men in charge? We see little progress in 2019. Even in this century, we are still far short of fifty-fifty representation. In the late 1600s and early 1700s, females like Mary Folger needed to rest content with a husband who took great risks for the natives and aimed to curb one form of white male supremacy. *A Looking Glass for the Times*, Peter's wife sensed, would inch the world forward toward gender justice one day.

But back in our era, I demanded of my mother. "Why must women marry, or become tied to a wheel and termed spinster for life?"

Luna would sometimes sigh and explain. "Males expect gratitude from females for patriarchal protections, as men see them. To their minds, there is no distinction between a gift and a foot on a woman's neck."

"Not so long into the future," Mother's words foretold, "an indentured girl feels warm gratitude for her dear, kind husband. Mary will intrigue many for generations to come, even master of the pen, Herman Melville."

On Nantucket Island, we have seen the majestic beauty of the cobalt sea and viewed on our travels the gorgeous brick and beige cliffs of her fellow island across the way, Martha's Vineyard. There we saw, also, white male supremacy at work, with mere misty hints of how "It gets better."

We have heard our Mary speak of her life on these two great islands, many a time here by Pulpit Rock.

Now, today, we shall share the thrill of Mary's voice, calling to us once more by these Clark's Island shores.

CHAPTER 4

Mary

Mary Folger (1620–1704) born Morrell

I'VE BEEN THRILLED TO JOIN with fifteen fellow observers-in-flight, over many centuries' time. I, the fourth of the first four, had one real choice in life: to marry. Like three before me, and three after, I was officially wed to the father of my many children. Giving birth was considered by us all to be a woman's purpose in life.

Among us, I was the sole soul to be bought out of indentureship. Peter Folger was an admirable, kind, and wise man. For myself, therefore, I had no cause to complain. And Peter has said, more than once, that purchase of his Mary was "the best appropriation of money I ever made."

Perhaps Thomas Jefferson considered our lady number eight, Sally, the best property ever inherited. Along with Sally, there were many other slaves inherited from his wife's father, John Wayles. Wayles was the owner of a vast southern plantation and had fathered Sally by her half-white mother, herself fathered by a slave ship captain. This added to a long list of African imported souls considered chattel. Sally was Martha Wayles Jefferson's half-sister, and three quarters white.

Jefferson never married or publicly acknowledged Sally as the mother of at least five of his children.

Why do I start with her story, not mine? We two have much in common. We were each officially owned by a man. We have lived what that is like.

Yet I was made free by a husband who bought me for twenty pounds sterling. Truly free? Only to the extent a married woman of my day could make such a claim. I could not own my own property. I could not participate in government of any kind.

I had to obey my husband, who could treat me however he chose, save for the rule of thumb. No beating was allowed, except by a stick smaller than that digit size. Not that my Peter had any such bent. Luckily for me, the Folgers did not subscribe to the same style of white male supremacy, as many of the day.

We all accepted the supremacy of white males over white females. It was not for centuries that Sarah Grimke, female advocate and slavery abolitionist, might become remembered for her brave public statement, "I ask no favor for my sex. All I ask of our brethren is that they take their feet off our necks."

In my day, in our beloved Massachusetts home, it was my husband who advised his brethren to take their feet off the necks of the natives. A century down the road, our grandson, Benjamin Franklin, held Peter's sentiments close in his heart when asking the British to take their feet off the necks of colonists in America. On our travels, we ladies all witnessed Ben, spectacles donned in Philadelphia, poring over my husband's *A Looking Glass for the Times*.

Should others who are listening to our tales in 2019 wish to learn more, perusal of Peter's poem might yield a fine snapshot of the day. If you have wondered, our descendants do indeed include founders of the company bringing you twenty-first century Folger's Coffee. Their travels took them from Nantucket Sound to San Francisco Bay during a great rush for gold.

As for those colors Joy says she sees flickering around me, those are colors of the sea. Nantucket, my dearest home and my final resting place, is surrounded by that blue sea, which protected my family and me. Centuries beyond, Melville had words of praise to offer.

"No good blood in their veins? They have something better than royal blood there. The grandmother of Benjamin Franklin was Mary Morrel; afterwards, by marriage, Mary Folger, one of the old settlers of Nantucket, and the ancestress to a long line of Folgers and harpooneers--all kith and kin to noble Benjamin--this day darting the barbed iron from one side of the world to the other."

We ladies hovered a while in 1851 to watch that master of the pen script his paean, *Moby Dick*. We watched a bit, as well, as Herman made friendship with Hawthorne, descendant of our Rebecca's nemesis, Judge Hathorne of those ghastly Salem trials. We saw Melville assure his fellow writer, Nathaniel, that his *The House of the Seven Gables* brought visible *truth* where greed, lies, and evil had once held sway.

But let us return to my own 1620 beginnings in the English village to which Joy and my fellow spirits traveled upon my 1704 passing. Joy and Shadow had greeted me with their tease, "It gets better." My reply, "I want to see," was met with welcome words. "Come with, then, dear Mary."

The gray skies of England hovered over the Morrell family, such that desperate gloom settled on my kind. Orphaned, I was offered an escape to Holland, then America, by way of my indenture to kindly Reverend Peters. He, the closest thing to a father in my years to come, was friend also to the Folger clan. Our trans-Atlantic voyage brought marvel and delight to my world, as in 1635 young Peter and I bonded in heart and mind. With Joy, Shadow, Anne, Elizabeth, and Rebecca, I could revisit many a heartwarming shipboard moment.

On this day of reminiscence in 2019, I shall savor again, nine years after that voyage across the pond, my first view of the Vineyard after my marriage in 1644. Leaving the mainland for a new lifetime of island adventures, our eyes were met with colors evoking gorgeous fall splendor. Year-round, at each crossing, earth tones, against a background of shimmering ocean blues, offered us welcome. Our lovely cliffs were painted with the same rood or rode tones, as the Dutch would say, as the Rhode Island coast we had left behind.

All nine of my children, but one, were born on Martha's Vineyard, where Peter could teach, preach, survey, build homes with and for others, serving as clerk as well as jack-of-all-trades. Then came our half-share of land on Nantucket, and a new home and birthplace for little Abiah. Nantucket was her haven, and mine. But we were never free from the fear of what would be our next trying time.

When Abiah was a tiny toddler two years of age, big sister Bethiah went to her watery grave. Of all crossings between the islands, that 1669 fearsome voyage took one child of my womb, to evermore haunt our souls.

There was our weary stretch of hardship in 1677, when Peter chose long months in jail, determined to protect the natives from greedy off-islander deceit. My husband refused to participate in perfidy against our local "Indian" friends. Clarence deftly imagined our thoughts on this stretch of solitude. For us, Clarence wrote the following words. "Mary," Peter said, "I believe I am beginning to get acquainted with myself. I never seemed to get around to it before."

"I hope," said Mary, "that you enjoy it as much as I have for thirty-three years." To this sentiment, I add in 2019 my present-day assent.

Listeners in 2019, or perhaps future readers, might ask: Who is Clarence? In our forward travels, we witnessed one of my many descendants laboring, in 1963, over a love story about my husband and me. Clarence King, in *The Half-Share Man*, expressed sentiments of an astute nature, to my mind, eerily reminiscent of my own. If curious for detail, I refer lovers of history to a 2014 re-publication by Clarence's great-grandson, William Alexander, who happened upon his great-grandfather's old tome.

Clarence ended his tale of Peter and me with a vignette from 1686, before the ghastly year 1692 reared its ugly head, drawing Abiah's big sister Bathshua into a terrible web. My poor middle girl, already of tortured mind, heard of all the Salem witch trial horrors, then pointed a finger at another of her own feminine kind. Rebecca!

By then, my youngest girl, Abiah, had found her heartstrings pulled taut by a wise and charming Josiah Franklin. Her match with the recently widowed man, ten years her senior, seemed made in heaven, poised to usher in happier times. And yes, soon there were more namesake grandchildren, coming to visit on island. Our son Eleazer, who had survived the storm that stole his sister from us, had soon married Sarah Gardner, and then fathered Folger offspring with the names of Peter, Mary, Sarah, and Nathan. There was an Eleazer Folger, junior, too. Everyone joyfully welcomed Abiah's darling babes, Peter, Mary, Sarah and James Franklin.

For me, I shall admit, Mary Franklin's arrival in 1694 was a much-celebrated blessing. That loving grandchild, bearing my first name, was sweet and smart like her mother! My little Mary was just ten years of age, at the time of my passing. Truly, I was sad to leave my grandchild, yet Joy filled my heart, when our leader and Shadow came to call. I had lived a long, full life, and was ready to go. Ready to see what was to come, for centuries down the road. Ready to see just how, "It gets better!"

Imagine my delight, when just ten years after Phillis joined Anne, Elizabeth, Rebecca and me, my granddaughter, Mary Franklin's baby sister, Jenny, numbered next amongst we who voyaged. In 1794, after a long life well lived, Jane answered the call of our leader, Joy. I, her grandmother, had not lived to see with mortal eyes the earthly arrivals of Abiah's last three, Benjamin, Lydia, and Jane. But then my youngest's youngest joined our growing gaggle, so that amongst ever-burgeoning numbers, she and I, together could travel. With our sister spirits, we would plumb the depths of American sights, through sunny days and cloudy, through wind, sleet and rain.

While flashing back in time with our Jane, we saw that for pretty little Jenny, next eldest brother Benny was her most treasured kin. Throughout her lifetime, his visits to Boston, and the many letters sent between them, would uplift her spirits, bringing comfort to soothe her many pains. Yet both Franklins, Ben and Jane, grieved deeply, sorely, we all saw on our travels, when big sister Mary died, breast cancer taking her away at an early age. She was thirty-six years, with two small children, in 1731 when she went to her grave.

More than a century later, there were thrilling sights to come. In 1847, after a full half of our sixteen had joined this witness party, we hovered near one of my many great-granddaughters, of the four-times-over ilk. Maria descended from the Folger line of Abiah's big brother, John. Girded by years of training at her astronomer father's side, this Mitchell daughter peered into her telescope, at just the right moment for us all. A comet discovered!

We came to know that "Miss Mitchell's Comet" was the first celestial body named for a woman in America. Decades beyond, in 1865, Vassar College for Women became home to my four times great-grandchild, proud female kin to Melville's vaunted, "noble Benjamin." At the Observatory there, she reigned for twenty years, a never-married female. Inspiring girls in search of knowledge, my descendant garnered many an accolade for her exploits, and received as guest, on Nantucket, other brilliants such as Melville, Emerson, Douglass, and Sojourner Truth. Summer travels with the Hawthorne family in Europe brought her rest and recreation.

It should be said that Peter and I, Maria's Folger ancestors, did not believe in infant damnation. As Baptists, we believed that grownup faith surely was required before baptism. Maria's family, Quaker-raised, practiced no baptism at all. Our Mitchell girl next chose the Unitarian belief, embracing a view that all are good. At Vassar, my brave descendant cast all chapel attendance aside and dove deep into Darwin's *The Origin of Species*. Maria blessed her pupils with avid astronomy teachings and many a memorable maxim. "Until women throw off their reverence for authority, they will not develop."

By 1873, assisting co-founders of The Association for the Advancement of Women became an added passion. In the end, what may be Maria's most enduring words remind us. "When we are chaffed and fretted by small cares, a look at the stars will show us the littleness of our own interests."

Yes, a soothing perspective might thus be found. Yet others of my four-times-great-granddaughters could find no such consolation. We have heard tell before, by this monument where male immigrants first worshipped, that our fellow traveler, Lucy, was the victim of insidious masculine supremacy. She whispered the truth on her deathbed, to her horrified and heartbroken husband. That was back in 1863, moments before she joined us.

In 1848, before Lucy's arrival but with half our number gathered, we lingered together over Seneca Falls. Elizabeth has made note of Lucretia, another of my bold Quaker great-granddaughters, four times over. Born a Coffin on my treasured Vineyard, she was descended through my son Eleazer, who survived that boating disaster in 1669. In 1811, my descendant Lucretia Coffin had married a Mott. She had hundreds of great-grandmothers, of course. It is not that I claim credit for her or her accomplishments. I merely marvel that there is such a thing as evolution, and that propagation of the species has yielded delightful results like Lucretia. By most in America in those days, human existence was credited solely to a white male God figure.

Yet because DNA had produced Lucretia, and bountiful others of her kind, matters about which we ancestors would never have dared complain were openly discussed on the floor of the Women's Rights Convention in 1848 -- to our joy! While working long ago at the Friends' School, where she met fellow teacher, James Mott, Lucretia had learned that she was paid far less than was he. This matter became just one of many 1848 grievances, about the status of females in those times.

Celebration of truly tangible progress under the law would have to wait another seventy-two years. Then, in 1920, Alice Paul could finally give the lie to her ancestor Governor John Winthrop's beliefs about a woman's place, which had fueled his wrathful banishment of our fellow traveler, Anne. Alice's own Quaker ancestry dated back to Governor William Penn and provided firm foundation for her successful efforts on behalf of the long-overdue female right to vote.

The result, the Nineteenth Amendment, yielded a giant step forward for womankind, and for men as well, in the United States of America. We ladies watched, entranced, as voters in their long skirts and fancy hats lined up at the polls, to cast their first ballot ever in a national election. Tuesday, November 2, 1920, has become an exceptionally joyful day in the memories of all gathered here in 2019.

For ten of us, those memories are posthumous. Of our six alive at the time, even Sarah, at age fourteen, was old and wise enough to appreciate that her life, like the lives of all females going forward in time, would be measurably improved. Yet Sarah saw, as well, how much was yet left to be done, as she carried forward the torch of the feminine search for independence.

As for Lucretia, paid less than her male counterparts, and all the many million females who came after, a president named Obama would sign the Leddy Ledbetter Fair Pay Act in 2009, aimed to make it "get better." Nearly a century after the Nineteenth Amendment, women vote, but still their pay is often three-quarters of their fellow man.

One other moment in 2009? A monument was erected and dedicated to me and my fellow female settlers of Nantucket, there for all to see at Founder's Burial Ground. That lovely spot is just up the way from the home where Peter and I lived out our days. Our ladies' fresh-faced stone now stands next to our husbands' weathered memorial, dedicated to the famous founding fathers 128 years prior to ours. Peter and nine others were paid their 1881 tribute with no mention of the natives whose land was acquired, by hook or by crook.

Descendants preferred to celebrate this early stage of America's march toward a white-male-led "Manifest Destiny."

But I slow the progress of our stories. We have yet to hear, on this fine August day, from fellow advocate of freedom, Phillis. It is time for advancement to our next introduction by Joy.

JOY 5

JUST AS I SPEAK WITH you, my fellow gatherers at Pulpit Rock, I have talks with Mother, still. "Is this real or imaginary?" I ask. Luna says that it matters not, then simply repeats the phrase we, too, utter often at our gatherings. "Time will tell."

As I lay at rest, eyes closed to bring me closer to her, questions tumbled out. "Was it really my choice to travel four hundred years into the future?"

"Could I really say 'no' to a role as wife and mother in the sixteen-hundreds?"

"How did you correctly predict which way I would choose?"

Most often, Luna does not claim credit for herself. "Time knew. Time told."

"Will America truly lead the world to gender-equal governing?" I asked frequently. Mother often replied in oblique fashion. One day, she commenced with a reminder of an ancient roadblock to equality in the New World.

"Do you recall what you have heard me say about Phillis? Slavery brought her to the eastern seaboard. There, just as women were deemed unequal by English men, those with dark skin, by white male definition, were judged unworthy of equal status. All this was done in the name of self-serving, avaricious purpose.

"You have seen that selfish polarization take hold and grow. One side of the spectrum offers love and appreciation for each gender and for human beings of all colors. An opposite side breeds anger and dissatisfaction with those who appear different from the white male holy image.

"From love and appreciation, follow acknowledgement, acceptance, and inclusion. Anger and dissatisfaction yield demeaning, degrading dismissal. Those two sides continue their battle, now in 2019."

Soon Luna shifts to questions and some answers, a tumbling series of her own.

"Yet how has that worked out for those who judged themselves supreme? Laws treating people of color as chattel have been removed from the books. Principles have been amended to include voting rights for non-whites and voting rights for women."

"Has not light shone brightly on that unique style of American discrimination, and on that old slavery-day determination that black is bad, white is good, colored is lesser while light-skinned the greater? Have we not inched beyond those dark, dastardly, dim-witted days of yore?

"Have not countries elsewhere informed us, with their progress in race and gender? Governments in Iceland, and Sweden, and Holland's neighbor Belgium all have achieved advancements.

"Harken there in Belgium a brilliant Deputy Prime Minister! Gender quotas in government is his message for all. "We should stop thinking the best are only men," is de Croo's trumpeted call. To a twenty-first century world, he offers *The Age of Women: Why Feminism Also Liberates Men*.

"Do you believe progressive steps in America will come to a halt? That voters in 2020 will stay home from the polls, failing to move forward? Or will they show up in force, choosing equal acceptance, regardless of color or gender, overcoming angry opposition to women and to the darker-skinned, leading in government?"

It is I, now answering my mother, Luna.

"Time will tell."

For all of us gathered today, time has sped us through four centuries. Each of you, as have I, had places to go, people to see, and moments when we gladly slowed. We hovered, we wept, we laughed, we learned. Then off we went, on more swift travels. Always to return, yearly, to our treasured summer gathering.

Now it is time to hear, once more, the colorful tale of another woman in our ranks. Dear Phillis, whose presence, for me, purely and perpetually, conjures the royal color purple. Please grace us, once more, with lessons from your times.

CHAPTER 5

Phillis

Phillis Wheatley Peters (1753–1784) born (African name unknown)

AS WAS TRUE FOR OUR dear Rebecca, I, too, am done with meek compliance. I have tended to tell my tale in timely order. Where to start? "At the beginning, of course," conventional wisdom advises. Not today. Not in 2019. Here again at Pulpit Rock, where a group of self-styled saints first gathered to shower their white male Christian god with gratitude, I choose to defy such conventions. Like Rebecca, I start elsewhere.

For me, among my earthbound recollections, the middle galls the most.

I have said before and will say again: There were exceptionally small-minded men, even and especially including extraordinarily tall John Hancock! Can you believe him, joining that gathering in our hometown of Boston, to grill me on my knowledge of literature, history, Greek and Latin?

Ah, yes. He, they all, feigned kindness and charm. They patronized me with promises that telling the "truth" (meaning telling the lies they hoped to hear) would bring no harm to me, a lowly female, a less-than-human dark-skinned creature. To them, I was nothing more than a slave, the property of John Wheatley, investor, tailor, constable, a man fully entrenched in their world of business.

I shall never forget Master Hancock rising to pace the room, looming over me as he tried, one final time, to get me to say it was not I who wrote my poems. Nor does the image fade in my mind today, of his stony, cold-faced fury as I answered with my own thoughts and beliefs, and spoke of how I had chosen to put them with pen to paper.

I would say his face darkened like black storm clouds, but the paleness of his skin does not allow. I recall each male visage turning a range of shades from politely pink to pastel purple as they realized, to the apparent distress of all, that they might have to admit I was capable of thought processes perhaps more eloquent than even their own.

"You are someone's puppet!" Master John had so dearly believed. "Tell us who put you up to this desire to be published, to be named as authoress of these works, and your own dissembling shall be pardoned." Those bits and pieces of my own mid-life mortal existence, from so long ago, have not lost their sting.

You fellow gatherers have heard tell of my subsequent voyage, urged by my owner's wife Susannah, across the seas with her son. He was a true gentleman, my "brother from another mother," Nathaniel Wheatley.

In London there was, truth be told, a publisher capable of recognizing quality in my writings who thought them worthy of international dissemination. My humble offerings speak mainly of others, yet one piece serves well as reminder of my full life story. Toward that end, today, I shall repeat:

Twas mercy brought me from my Pagan land,
Taught my benighted soul to understand
That there's a God, that there's a Saviour too:
Once I redemption neither sought nor knew.

Some view our sable race with scornful eye,
"Their colour is a diabolic dye."
Remember, Christians, Negroes, black as Cain,
May be refin'd, and join th' angelic train.

How did it all end? My short answer: In a visit from Joy! As was the case with each of you in our Clark's Island sisterhood, she and Shadow called to me, "It gets better!" Then, when I answered, "I want to see," "Come with" was her quick reply.

What preceded my final passing to the great beyond? There is a story or two to tell.

Our sister spirit, Jane, had a famous brother, Benjamin. He called her Jenny, she called him Benny. Master Franklin was there in London, at the time of my visit to my publisher, and came to see me. I had grown used to calls from and to men in charge of great affairs of the world. I'd received my invitation to meet the Queen! Most emissaries emanated varying degrees of supercilious attention to my existence. Mister Franklin seemed to be cut from a special cloth.

I never would have said, yet I sensed that affable Master Franklin might agree that the God of whom we all spoke, the God whose name I evoked so frequently in my writings, need not be imagined as male, nor as white-skinned. As Joy and Luna have helped us all come to know, there is something far greater than all those mortal trappings. Our true guiding force, a light within and without, can be viewed as the sun, as powerful and with eternal love for all. A belief in that life force is no better and no worse than what any Christian may profess.

But try telling that to a 2019 evangelist. Try explaining my own beginnings across the seas on the continent of Africa. There, we worshipped the sun. Yet my terrifying capture by fellow natives and my excruciating voyage in a ship's hold in brutal heat amidst vomit and excrement? That left me ready to adopt whatever creed might best guarantee my survival. I was just a girl in her seventh year!

The men in charge in my new land believed in a Christian God as creator of all, some six thousand years prior. So, too, would I.

Mr. Benjamin Franklin, well positioned among white males of his time, was free to speak of "God" while foregoing weekly or daily routines of organized religion. His sister, our fellow traveler Jane, and I were far better served to profess beliefs shared with church-going Christians of the day. A woman, far more than any man, had best convince herself and others that the Holy Bible held the one true word of the one true God.

And that god, rest assured, must be called "He," or risk the fate of our fellow traveler, Anne, an accused and banished "heretic." As we meet in 2019, it seems that such patriarchal realities still linger for many females.

I shall not bore you with a full repeat of the highs and lows of my life after my Christian-affirming publication, *Poems on Various Subjects, Religious and Moral*. No time to meet the Queen, though I had been invited. I made hasty return to Boston, to tend to my beloved Mistress Susannah Wheatley as she lay dying. I was granted freedom. I married a sweet-hearted, hardworking man, a doctor whose dark skin played an inexorable role in a voyage to the poor house. My two babies died soon after birth. I passed alone and penniless. These scant details paint enough of my picture.

Then Joy arrived, as you all know. With her, Shadow, Anne, Elizabeth, Rebecca, and Mary, I witnessed innumerable lives playing out, just as Luna foretold. Soon it was 1794, and time to go back to Boston, to find not Susannah, but Jane, as she lay dying.

I defer now to Joy, all the sooner to bring us our next life story, the tale of Ben's sister Jenny. Like her famous brother, Jane seems always to have savory treats for heart and mind.

JOY 6

We thank you again, Phillis, for your tale. Each telling reminds us of just cause to yearn.

"Will America truly lead the world to gender-equal government?" I asked throughout my childhood. With each story told, Mother always, directly or by hint, suggested that very outcome. It was just such a world my beating heart came to crave.

Yet only men voted in Plymouth and in Duxbury. Only men voted to the north in Boston. Only men were elected Governor, to represent all within the New England colonies of Plymouth and Massachusetts.

In 1614, Captain John Smith had been the first to map the shores he named for the motherland of these invading white men.

By 1638, new maps had carved the northern landscape, where Luna and I lived with the Aldens in Duxburrow, from more southern lands of Plymouth, where we had stayed with the Warrens. One village had become two.

Mother's tales were always laced with future knowledge of the world. Her lessons in biology endlessly fascinated my own young mind, conjuring parallels to the world around me. In summer I witnessed matings of cow and bull in the field. Spring brought births of baby calves.

Future studies, Luna informed, use a gadget called "microscope." Peering inside, a man, a woman too, could bear witness to asexual reproduction. One cell could be seen dividing itself, becoming two.

"Like Plymouth and Duxbury?" I queried. Her laughter was kindly. "Yes, my child. That you could say."

Luna's lessons continued, "We humans are sexual beings, with two genders who mate, as do cats, dogs, and cows."

"Will it stay that way, with male and female required, to yield offspring?"

"For thousands of years to come, for as long as can be seen, our species will need one egg from a woman, one sperm from a man, one coming together of the two, for a child to be born." I loved learning, through the eyes of my prescient mother, of the inner workings of such things.

As my mother's only child, I adored learning, as well, of future human matings, especially when resulting offspring are family to me. Jane Franklin, whose story comes next on this day, is my niece, Luna explained. Her brother, Ben, is my nephew. My father, Thomas, is their grandpa. My half-brother, Josiah, their candle-maker father.

"You share a great curiosity about the world," Mother told me, at each mention of the Franklin name. "No one knows now of a thing called electricity. Yet the fellow who shares with you what will become known as DNA, Jane's brother, Ben, will take his kite into a raging storm to learn of such matters, despite great peril to his own life on earth."

"If we cannot yet see or know of this thing called electricity," I mused, "perhaps we cannot yet see or grasp an idea like gender-equal government?"

"Out of the mouths of babes," Luna chortled, not for the first or last time.

"How does Jenny fit into our tales of women throughout four hundred years of history in America?" one might ask. When she joined us in 1794, and traveled with us back to her girlhood days, we all agreed, "What a pretty child."

A yellow ray of sunshine greets my eye, as I recall Jane's voyage onward through early years. Her charms did not go unnoticed by local boys, Ed Mecom among them. In their day, a book titled, *"Why is Sex Fun?"*, a work from the 1990s by the ever-elucidating Jared Diamond, indubitably would have been banned in Boston.

The "Evolution of Human Sexuality," as that subtitle explains in Jared's twentieth century publication, dates back through millennia. We see clarified, in part, why in 1727, our sunny Jenny was with child and then promptly married. One hundred years after immigrant women in Plymouth had borne children, little had changed for females in Jane Franklin's world. As bounty of her beauty, she would give birth a dozen times over, as her sunlight faded to sanguine silver.

"Was our Jenny a mere baby machine? Or did she, does she have her own thoughts? Does she have a voice?"

Yes, I shall attest. Each time she has spoken, here by our glacial monument, flashes of sunflower and maize make their mark. As do our fellow traveler's words and cheery humor. Speak again, dear Jane, and prove me right.

CHAPTER 6

Jane

Jane Mecom (1712–1794) born Franklin

AH, THE PRESSURE, DEAR JOY. Every year, must I be witty, like my brother Ben? What saying might best apply? A woman's work is never done! Then expect no thanks, from anyone.

Over this last half century, as we ladies gather annually, our chronicles reveal four centuries of male dominance in America. Some in this twenty-first century world believe that is what makes America great.

Yet, as our stories and twenty-first century custom still show, it is members of our sex who have prettied themselves, married the males, borne the children, fed them and their fathers, cleaned our homes, darned the socks, healed the sick, buried babies who passed, tended the old, washed the windows, gone to market, with never an end in sight.

My husband, a maker of saddles, struggled to bring home the bacon, to earn a smidgeon or two. More often than not, the bar called him from such mundane pursuits. I hasten to make clear, the name Edward Mecom did not end with Esquire. It was a Boston pub to which he fled, coming home more than once to rage, then cry and repent his fury. Yet, a man's home is his castle, is it not? Did Ed not have every right to rant?

My brother, more than most, lived up to a male ideal. He deeply respected his mother, sisters, and life partner Deborah. Still, it was Deborah's devotion to countless quotidian matters that allowed him to pursue his brilliant path in history. She tended their business in Philadelphia, while raising Will, his son by another woman, and their daughter, Sally. Both children would become respected citizens in their times. Will was Colonial Governor of New Jersey, though also a Loyalist who fled to Britain during the war. Sally was wife of Richard Bache, a hostess for her father in support of the Revolution, and mother of eight.

How to describe Benny? Well, I must say I am proud of my brother's countless contributions to life in the seventeen, eighteen, and nineteen hundreds. In 2019, as we ladies marvel at the sight of big screen televisions flashing shows of all kinds, we see advertisements galore. There he is again! An ad on your money channel, as we call it, has my sibling's image lauding a company called Franklin Templeton Investments, listed on the New York Stock Exchange under the ticker "BEN." Yes, in honor of my brother, Benjamin Franklin. Not to mention, I make note to all others following our tales, my brother's image on your one-hundred-dollar bill.

So that her husband could achieve his astounding accomplishments, Deborah's work was never done. Her reward? Death by stroke, at age 66, while her loving yet wandering husband, who would live to age 84, traveled abroad. The language of ancient and present-day white male supremacy does not even truly acknowledge her gender.

Quite the contrary. As the word of God elucidated, we ladies, starting with Eve, were made from one small rib of Adam. That fellow got to be a man. His appendage, Eve, was merely wo-man. He had his own titles, such as male. She a mere subcategory, fe-male. As a boy, we might call him lad. She, a lass, might graduate only to lad-y. Need I go on?

As for me, I am merely "Ben's sister, Jenny." Were it not for my famous brother, no one would ever have heard of me. What's more, I could not spell, to my dismay! That is to say, I could not spell well. A few of my letters to Benny were saved and they prove my point. Yet I could think. Sometimes, I claim, I could think well. To write well, it has been said, one must first think well. So, spelling be damned. I could, at least on occasion, write well.

Yet in my day, girls learned to aspire otherwise. Be first a beauty, God willing.

Still, "Beauty is as beauty does," our Joy heard Luna opine.

When you ladies joined me in my times, you could see Brother Benjamin had warning words of a similar kind. I do not tire to recall the comfort to be found by me, baby sister, in missives from big brother Ben. Yet such matters also gall. "Why do the boys and men get to be in charge of all things written?" Many a female had a like complaint.

Throughout our lives I watched and waited, right there in Boston, as one man's life evolved into fame. Runaway. Printer. Publisher. Thinker. Shopkeeper. Library maker. Voyager. Inventor. First Postmaster General. Ambassador. Diplomat. Founding Father. And most dangerous man in America, to British eyes.

I say again to my companions, and to the world today, if you want the sad story of a humble Boston soap-maker, taking in boarders in order to get by, Harvard professor extraordinaire, Jill Lepore, has done right by me in her *Book of Ages*. The charming jacket, with a portrait of my dearest granddaughter Jenny, gives me thrills to see. My heart warms with the memory of that darling blue-eyed child, grasping a pink flower, in the artist's imagined dress of mustard yellow.

I have no complaints, only deep appreciation for Jill's kind attention to my kind, and to my life story. My fellow travelers have heard varied details from me over time. Others can search out Lepore for more, should they care.

Today, I shall make note, once again, of Benny's letter about beauty and beaus. It seems my brother hoped to spare me marriage at fifteen. Whatever his hopes, I was married and fated to bear twelve children. Four went as babies to the grave, two more died well before their time, to my mind. I survived all my offspring but one, daughter Jane.

"That is how it is, for now" Luna replied more than once, when her daughter repeated that lament, "Why are only men in charge?" Born near a century beyond Joy's birth, that is exactly how it was for me, too. I was meant to perform my female duties, then disappear from view. No memorial for Ben's baby sister. After my death, my home was demolished to make room for a monument to the great Paul Revere.

Religion? I was truly a conformist in my day. Yet looking back on my submerged status, along with fellow females, in four hundred years of this country's history? Religion played a powerful role, as a tool to devalue women, is what I shall now brave to say.

Meanwhile, a man like my brother Ben Franklin is known and admired around the world, as we speak at our annual gatherings. Still, there is our cause, championed by Joy and all who had joined her, promising me a better life for all, at my passing.

"It gets better," I was told on that gray day in May 1794.

"I want to see," was all fellow travelers needed to hear.

"Come with," I was offered.

So here I am, in another round, eager for the future, and for fine new words from our Joy!

JOY 7

"WHY DO WE HAVE A king?"

Throughout our days with the Warren family, then with the Alden clan, in each spare moment I presented my mother with such queries. Replies from Luna never failed to elucidate.

"Why do dogs and cats have tails? And does the tail wag the dog, or the dog wag the tail?" Mother replied. For often her answers started with questions. Those were always tasty food for thought. A main course likely followed.

"We have kings to remind us that boys and men are taller and physically stronger than girls and women. Their size has always kept men in charge." To her answer, Mother added a caution. "We must do what the king tells us to do. We must do what Master Alden says."

I recalled Luna's tales of kings wielding power over all their lands, backed by vast armies sporting men of great size and strength, row after row. Battles lasted for days. Wars lasted for years, decades, even a century long.

"Will this always be?"

Mother had often suggested not, but I was eager to hear more.

"The day will come when a nuclear code replaces the masculine hold on power."

Ah! Intriguing. You fellow travelers might easily guess my own next words.

"What is a nuclear code?!"

"It will take centuries to develop such a thing. Studies in science will advance, just as we sentient beings have evolved. Unlike cats and dogs, we no longer require a tail."

I giggled.

Then Luna's face grew serious.

"A descendant of Mistress Warren, after classic studies in Europe of a science known as chemistry, will partner in the development of an emerging field. That newborn realm of chemical engineering, hand in hand with Fermi's passion, atomic and particle physics, will help lead the way to a nuclear code. The secret 1940s venture, led by Oppenheimer and later named the Manhattan Project, is why, one day, we shall no longer require a masculine system of government."

An abrupt end followed Mother's nourishment for my fascinated brain. Luna had work to do, with Mistress Alden, to prepare the evening repast. I had my own chores, with little Ruth in tow.

Today, meeting at Pulpit Rock in 2019, we feast our minds on oft-told tales of old.

Abigail, you will share your story next. Once more, the flavor, the sound, the succulent sight your speech conjures, will sweep us right with you to heart-wrenching moments. Images of deep red quince, when cooked to make tasty jam, flash for me each time I hear your tale.

You loved John Adams deeply, yet what a challenge he could be!

My favorite Alden child, Ruth, bears credit for your husband's presence in your life, for your children's existence. On our travels, I thrilled to see Ruth in 1657, in Braintree, share vows with John Bass, the son of Deacon Samuel and Mistress Ann Bass.

Decades, generations flew by. Another courtship, another wedding. In 1764, we found you two, you and John Adams, ensconced in Braintree, just south of Boston and right by Quincy, which was named for your grandfather. The men in your Quincy line could read, write, and opine with the best of their kind.

No wonder you and John were inextricably drawn to each other.

Centuries later, in 2005, we who travel would see biographer Grant shower your husband with praise. "John Adams was a superb writer. Abigail, at her best, was better," that twenty-first century author opined, without pause.

As for me, I now shall pause in this Pulpit Rock moment, to yield the floor to our venerable Abby.

CHAPTER 7

Abigail

Abigail Adams (1744–1818) born Smith

IN THE 1630S, JOY ASKED Luna, "Why do we have a king?" In our era, many pondered in similar fashion. We did so with growing vigor in the 1760s and 1770s.

My husband and I silently asked ourselves, even openly queried each other, "Why do we tolerate this King and his abuses?!"

For no one was more crazy than old King George.

Each time I speak by this great granite gift from the glacier age, I rejoice that in the end, we Americans could, and did, throw off the yoke of submission to royalty. Yet for females, I must still sadly observe that male tyranny continues to thrive.

Why, just the last year, in 2018, we saw a man named Kavanaugh made supreme, in the highest court of our land, ignoring a woman's truthful, sometimes teary testimony. You were so brave, Christine Blasey Ford!

I am reminded of my own husband's response to my written plea as he, Thomas, and Ben earned their titles. Founding Fathers of America, they would become. A Declaration of Independence was in the works. A Constitution would follow, designed to preserve the patriarchy.

Please, "Remember the Ladies," I asked. I cautioned further, "We will not hold ourselves bound by any Laws in which we have no voice, or Representation."

"I cannot but laugh," Mr. Adams replied.

"Depend upon it, we know better than to repeal our Masculine Systems," added the man who had vowed to love, honor, and cherish.

You have heard, more than once, how this galled me.

My promise that women would rise in rebellion, if not duly heard was met with derision. Claiming, in any case, to hold "only the Name of Masters," John dismissed my plea. "Despotism of the Peticoat," was the ghastly danger my husband decried.

These masculine fears live on through the ages. Females remain throttled by a faulty system. We who meet here yearly, we see a path to freedom. A system that is equal, for each gender, will one day become written.

Our task, our 2020 mission, is giving birth to that beautiful, glorious new world.

My own story? That is of little matter, here in 2019. So much has already been written and preserved, to be easily found in a long list of places. Start, if you will, up the road in Quincy. Or at my birthplace in Weymouth.

It is Sally, of whom I wish to speak, before yielding back to Joy. What Tom's "servant," as I discreetly termed her, may choose to say this gorgeous New England day, I know not. But memories haunt me, of a time when our fellow traveler, Thomas Jefferson's slave, came to England. Sally was a frightened girl, no older than a twentieth-century Christine when a teen-aged Kavanaugh left her so afraid.

Sally's master's daughter, Polly, came with the slave girl. It was hard to tell who was more terrified. It was ludicrous for Sally to be the nanny. Upon parting, we all cried, for Tom was determined that both must come to him in France. We all know now what followed. Upon return in 1789 to our newborn United States, Sally was with child.

Even today, two-hundred-and-thirty years later, there are laws in which women have had little voice, due to lack of true and equal representation for our gender. Kavanaugh demanded sympathy for himself, not for Christine. Trump, with an all-male phalanx of Republican committee members, saw to it that the Masculine System continues to reign.

Here and now, I shall end my say, for today, with a final, haunting thought. Poor child, my heart still breaks at the pitiful sight of innocent Sally, which forever comes to mind. It is burned in the hippocampus.

JOY 8

"WHY MUST I ALWAYS WEAR this cumbersome coif?" I muttered many a time in girlhood.

I recall one motherly reply. Luna spoke to me, then, of unspeakable acts. She gave meaning to our saying, "Truth be told." Luna spoke, also, of proper context.

"Skin on skin, a sensual touch, those precious moments are worth their weight in gold in proper context." So I was assured.

"Yet, sad to say, boys and men may take without asking at times. Then they explode with excuses and blame a victim. Yes, a girl or woman might be blamed for her beauty. Your coif is a gesture, aimed to obscure one of many sights said to tempt. Those female locks, whether black or brunette or golden, are said to be woman's crowning glory."

Yet I did not indulge in self-blame when I sadly learned my own truth. I, too, would fall victim to male misuse of size and of power over the female gender. Did I cause this intrusion, by having cast my coif aside on a lovely, lone walk on a Duxbury trail? It seemed clear to me; it was silly to pardon him his crime. Yet others would not easily agree, so his secret became safe with me.

For a slave girl, like Sally, size is no matter. His position, as master, that is what requires submission by her, to all of his desires. Any question of assent is easily swept aside. Yet both of them are mired in secrecy. For tens of generations there will come endless denials.

For our Sally, there was much confusion. Her context? Opposites and illusion. Black or white? Slave or free? Good or bad? Valued or devalued, by her Master, by the world?

There in France, she had no mother to guide her. No words of wisdom to help her decide. Return to America, or stay and be free? How could a girl of fifteen make such a choice in a world where only men are in charge?

We know today that Thomas Jefferson got his way. Sally's children were so much like him, that seeing was believing. And centuries beyond, the truth emerged through a thing called DNA.

"Will we girls ever be free of this burden?" I moaned more than one time. Luna, who saw clearly centuries of glacial progress to come, explained to me in my girlhood.

"There is a long, hard path ahead," Mother cautioned. "But one day, yes, justice will be ours and yours. You may choose to journey forward, bearing a much-needed message, or choose to marry in the here-and-now," Luna always promised. "Perhaps a child you bear might bear none of her own, to serve instead the purpose you have been offered."

"Or perhaps you, alone, can seize this moment to ultimately save the day?" Mother, as I have said, did not seek credit for her vision, nor claim perfection for her power to portend. What never failed was Luna's gift to inspire my thoughts about my awesome choice. Love and marriage? Or a four-hundred-year journey with fellow women through the ages?

As much as I felt maternal-like love for little Nathaniel, or romantic love for Thomas Southworth, all paled in contrast to Shadow.

Shadow! Silly, you might say. A seagull? A bird?

Of course, he was much more, as time would tell. Yet, always, our connection was founded, I claim, on shared knowledge that we were viewed by the white males of Plymouth as lesser beings. As were all my fellow females, then and, if truth be told, now in 2019.

Sally, too, was and still is deemed less. Grateful as she may be to Master Jefferson for her offspring, love between equals was not an option for them or their children in their day. The world was, and is, not yet color equal and, exponentially true, was and is not yet gender equal, either.

Our girl was a toddler of a mere three years and newly arrived at Monticello when her master, upon return from Pennsylvania Colony, carefully stored his copy of precious cargo. A document titled "A Declaration" claimed independence for colonists in America, freeing white males, and by association their women, from the despair of despotism. Thomas Jefferson's slave boy had been there as well, in the city of Philadelphia, and whispered of hot humid days. He watched as Master Benjamin Franklin and Master John Adams came and went. Silently delivering daily sustenance, the lowly colored boy served the man who wrote, "all men are created equal." His slave prepared the author's bed for brief moments of rest, as Master Jefferson wrote, and wrote, and re-wrote.

Like his friend and sometime foe Adams, Tom knew not to "repeal our Masculine Systems." Those privileged white-male-dominated systems. Yes, whites only in Independence Hall. Males only as well, when signatures were put to parchment on that great Declaration.

The definition of white? The tiniest of black blood rendered any human, male or female, "of diabolic dye" to the white male eye of 1776. Why did not the tiniest of white blood render him or her white and "refined?" Why could not our Sally, three-quarters the same as Tom, be known as part of the "angelic train?" Why was Phillis's "sable race" not the one in charge?

"Why must these more colorful women suffer added indignities, far beyond those of us deemed to be white?" I asked Luna as she told tales of like females to come.

Phillis has said she wondered at white male perceptions which ruled in her times. We fellow voyagers have all marveled, so many centuries later, at government hearings where a Kavanaugh and his masculine defenders united in determined white male dominance, over women both white and of color. Sally, too, knew full well the cold, hard realities

71

of the seventeen and eighteen-hundreds. There would be no repeal of definitions of race, or of white male supremacy, for centuries to come.

Even this past year, we ladies heard an elected member of Congress named Steve King ask, "White supremacist – how did that language become offensive?" A small slap on his wrist followed this utterance of lingering belief from ages past. As for the sitting President, Trump's insults to those darker of skin than he are met with laughter from some and mere rolling of eyes from those who could dissent had they not been rendered anaesthetized by the man's endless diatribes.

Yet dignity defines our historical ladies of color. Phillis, so royal in her ways, that frequent purple flashes greet my eyes each time she takes her turn among us. When Sally speaks, it is a royal tone I also see, a more fuchsia hue, attesting to the beauty of her soul.

Let us hear, again, from our Sally.

CHAPTER 8

Sally

Sally Hemings Wayles (1773–1835) (slave inherited by Jefferson)

LIKE OUR FELLOW VOYAGER, PHILLIS, there is a moment which, for me, galls above others. This came long after my passing, near the end of our journey through time, right in this twenty-first century. Despite countless facts uncovered in the 1900s, DNA tests and all, in 2001, Lance Banning asked, "Case Closed?" Then that privileged white male want-to-be-prophet saw fit to conclude, "the proper verdict, at this moment, has to be 'not proven'."

To the mind of Mr. Banning, we must believe in the "character" of that famed ancestor, Thomas Jefferson. The father of my children would never stoop, Lance believed, to mate with a woman of color.

"Terrified," Abigail said. Yes, I was, shivering and fearful of my lot in 1787. That was when I first met our fellow voyager, known then as Mrs. John Adams. I so well recall a moment when I was a slight, light-skinned child of fourteen or so, clinging to Abigail as much, if not more than my lily-white charge.

Polly, she's my niece if truth be told, had lost her mother Martha, as had Patsy, the eldest of the two daughters and barely older than I. For me, Mistress Jefferson, the daughter of John Wayles, was a kind, if distant, secret half-sister, gone early to her grave. In London, John Adams' wife reported my sad truth by letter, to Thomas, her diplomat friend in France. I, putative nurse to Polly, might "need more care" than Tom's own child, four or five years the younger. Patsy, ensconced in Paris with her father, still innocently enjoyed her privileged white world.

My brother James, like me fathered by Wayles but, as was the custom, given our mother Betsy's surname of Hemings, was settled also in Paris. James served the Master in the Jefferson household. Two years later, when the Revolution deemed slavery unlawful in France, we each could have remained there, free. But I was with child. Thomas promised freedoms of other kinds, if I would but return to the newborn United States with him, my infatuated Master.

How had we reached that moment? For early origins, I rely on family lore. My grandmother arrived in chains. After violent capture in Africa, carried away over raging seas, she survived that virulent voyage in a dark ship's hold. The sea captain who by way of this journey fathered my mother, Elizabeth, was a white man, named John Hemings. Secret mixing of races resulted from this trip to American shores. My grandmother remains known simply and sadly as Unnamed African Woman.

Half-white Elizabeth, my mother Betsy Hemings, was chosen by Virginia plantation owner John Wayles, for fathering of half-a-dozen children of even more mixed race. I, three-quarters-white Sarah, known as Sally, was born the youngest in 1773. I am told that was the year of Sea Captain John Heming's death. It will be no wonder we might all remain dazed and confused about those torturous details.

Since my 1776 arrival at Monticello, as property inherited by the Jeffersons via Thomas's wife, Martha, I remember well many a firsthand detail. A Richmond newspaper, in 1802, told my story, meant to breed horror, of my merger with Master Tom. He would neither confirm nor deny. Others did then and do now rush to climb on a high horse in eager "defense," claiming the most blessed of the patriarchs was far above mixing races.

I refer to the title of a 2018 tome by true defenders of truth, Annette Gordon-Reed and Peter S. Onuf. I conclude that near all one needs to know is to be found in *"Most Blessed of the Patriarchs": Thomas Jefferson and the Empire of the Imagination*. To any question of, "Was it love between Thomas Jefferson and Sally Hemings?" I would only add the following.

Silly question! A white master, thirty years my senior, and I, a slave girl of fourteen years? Love is not possible when overpowering fear rules the day. Perhaps decades later, when my daughter Harriet and my son Beverly were given leave, as promised, to disappear into the white world of America.

My youngest boys, Madison and Eston, were freed in 1826, as sworn by POTUS 3 in his will, and then my sons protected me in their Charlottesville home. Since my death in Virginia in 1835, I have joined my fellow females in travels until this pleasant August day. One-hundred-and-eighty-four years' worth – yielding a treasure chest of memories with priceless pieces to ponder.

A move by both my youngest children to Ohio and life in a state somewhat free of slavery's scourge, evoked no surprise, yet brought proud pleasure to savor. Then Anne, Elizabeth, Rebecca, Mary, Phillis, Jane, Abigail, and I, with Joy and Shadow, all witnessed the wonder of a new family home in Madison, Wisconsin. Why did Eston leave brother James Madison Hemings, and a long list of nieces and nephews behind in Chillicothe to live out their Ohio years as colored folk?

In 1852, Eston, with his wife Julia Isaacs Hemings and their two boys and one girl, adopted the Jefferson name. They disappeared into whiteness, among new fellow citizens of Wisconsin. Eston was four years gone to his grave by the 1860 census and we saw the Assistant Marshal count widow Julia and her grown boys as white. Eldest son, John W. Jefferson, was "Hotelkeeper," with his real and personal estate valued at a total of $16,300. Youngest boy, Beverly was "Barkeep" in their bountiful business endeavor.

My daughter-in-law and grandsons ran this Madison hotel with a Bavarian bellboy and Irish domestic Mary O'Brienn amongst a large number of Norwegian cooks and servants. English and Germans were peppered amidst other whites born in Vermont, New York, Massachusetts, or Ohio. Not a hint of color, throughout staff or hotel guests, or in this Jefferson family.

What a blessing, to be able to follow the paths of my youngest children, and those grandchildren, on their own voyages through American history. However, it was sad to see that Eston's relationship to former President Thomas Jefferson was hidden, so that my grandsons, brothers John and Beverly Jefferson, might hide "tainted" blood. Master Jefferson and Martha had no sons to bear his name, yet male progeny of POTUS 3 were quite real, as we know. None were pure white, leaving my boys to be viewed as born of shame.

Still, because of Joy, I could bear witness ten years down the road, back in Ohio, to the proud proclamation of our truth in 1870, in the latest United States census. Census taker Weaver filled his Chillicothe pages with script of great beauty, in style and content. With careful attention to detail, William Weaver makes note of Madison Hemings, age 65: "This man is the son of Thomas Jefferson."

I hear myself speak those words to you, my fellow voyagers, and return in an instant to a scene back in the day. Retired from presidential travails, Tom took to furniture-making, and to training his now teenage sons in that same fine craft. "Uniformly kind" to everyone, are the words Madison would one day use. It was a rare moment for me to happen upon the boys at work with the man they well knew to be their father. It afforded an indelible thrill to my heart.

His murmured words, his kindly glance, his careful, considered touch, caught my eye like a gift from the goddess of good. Joy was followed by peace in my soul, at this proof of a promise kept. Thomas had done what he set out to do, all those years back when I was too young to dare pretend I could know. He did love me, and our children, with depth beyond measure. This blessed knowledge settled softly in my quickly beating heart.

And that is why I put forth to you, in 2019, another 2018 moment of bearing witness. At long last, all the world was welcome to view my truth, my reality with Thomas Jefferson and our children, at graceful, gorgeous Monticello.

A whole exhibit, completed after decades of reunions and rancor, followed by ultimate reconciliation. MonticelloCommunity.org tells us that there is much more we all need to witness. There the world can see added proof of due respect, as Thomas stepped ever closer to his boys. He loved his violin and gifted like instruments to both our youngest. Lessons learned from the patriarch led to lives filled with music for amateur musician Eston and professional musician Madison. The magic of such sights and sounds will speak of our truth through the ages.

How did our honest family history finally meet the light of day? The births of a sister and brother, Julia and John, were crucial steps to the ultimate DNA key. Julia was twelve when baby brother John West Jefferson was born in 1946. We ladies joined her, an eager young girl in Evanston, Illinois, as her father and her mother followed her by car, having discovered her plan to bicycle to a new black friend's home. They intercepted their daughter and we witnessed a stern parental rebuke, as Julia's bike was placed in the car's trunk, for a return ride home. "Keep to your own kind," is the message those Jefferson parents insistently conveyed.

Who are *they*? What *is* their kind? A family secret remained hidden until 1976, when descent from my son Eston leapt into view. Yet twenty-two more years passed before Julia heard from a Dr. Foster, wishing for access to Jefferson Y DNA. A phone number for baby brother John was proffered.

Amazing results were soon produced and announced to the world in the year 1998. The 2001 publication of *Jefferson's Children: The Story of One American Family*, brought dozens of voices together, from both of President Thomas Jefferson's families, white and colored. My Madison's five times great-grandson Shannon Lanier is the author of that book, along with Jane Feldman. Another Jefferson grandson many times over, numbered amongst Thomas's all-white progeny, Lucian K. Truscott IV, bravely writes the book's introduction. Truscott was denounced by some of his fellow all-white descendants. All three writers contend for a decade or more with horrified denials.

Meanwhile, The Monticello Community held their own mixed reunions over the years, at the home where my children, like Patsy and Polly, were born and raised. June of last year was a joyful sight with descendants of all colors in blue and white. This year, 2019, even the Monticello Association, holder of gravesite rights, might finally be coming around to a new world view. Thus, our saga continues, and I shall savor each step forward toward liberty, toward the justice we are due.

Enough, now. Enough about me and mine.

For details on further delicate matters, let us once again give ear to Joy. She will bring us ever closer to our next story of struggle for women in America. Her introduction to Lucy is certain to open hearts and widen our eyes.

Time now for added sobering, serious history.

JOY 9

"Why must women and girls sit and listen, nearly all day long, as only men speak?"

Whether on Sabbath Day, or all the week long, I took every chance that arose to ask Luna once more. "Why so unfair?!"

From the Warren home, we trekked meekly up the way to meet on Sundays, the end of each week. From the Aldens in Duxburrow, for years, the family dutifully went south for a similar joint service.

"Why do we not see Mistress Warren or Mistress Alden speak in the Lord's name for all to hear?"

"Hush," my mother might need to reply, when within earshot of others. "We will speak together, you and I, later, dear child, on such matters."

When later came, Luna did her best to explain.

"This Plymouth church is like a family, led by the largest and strongest, led by a man. Just as Richard Warren and John Alden have always taken charge in their homes, a man, when all the families gather, must lead as patriarch and as defender of what is right and good. For our safety, this masculine system is a moat."

"For now," Mother cautioned, "we must not rock that boat."

So, I listened, quietly waiting, until music time. Then, at least, I could raise my voice and be heard, even if only in someone else's words.

A favorite of mine? That uplifting Dutch hymn, written to celebrate the end of war in the old country, where Mother had met my Franklin father.

"We Gather Together," warmed my heart every time.

Secretly, I altered the words in my mind. Then with Ruth, sang out loud, in the marsh, when back home.

"She hastens and chastens her will to make known."

I guess I always chaffed at patriarchy, with all the related pitfalls for humanity. Mother's stories of the future often fed my indignation, even as evidence of progressive evolution emerged. I would learn from Luna that an eighty-three-year-old Sigmund Freud, by the time of his death in 1939, had sowed seeds of new freedoms, through growing self-knowledge for males and females of those times.

Psychoanalysis was Freud's method. Transference, a priceless contribution to new concepts, which shed light on family and human relations. Lucy lived in an era long before the days of Freud and was a victim of transference, to my mind, as well as a victim of a scoundrel named Reverend Beecher, that abuser of male power. Shall we leap to her story?

Not yet, I must demur, for memories come to mind of nearly a decade after our Lucy joined us. By 1873, a long list of one-on-one discussions were observed by voyager Lucy, and by eight more traveling spirits, Shadow, and me, whether in a horse and carriage sitting at rest as the bustle of New York City lends background, or in a stately home as servants quietly proceeded with day or nighttime duties. There was bountiful proof of further Beecher betrayals, nearly a decade past our Lucy's death, which built Theodore Tilton's case against his friend and family preacher.

We would see that Victoria Woodhull had heard from the Reverend's sister, Catherine, though she would later recant; from his sibling Isabella, who staunchly concurred with Henry's many accusers; and from suffragists Susan Anthony and Mrs. Stanton, each on separate occasions. They knew full well that which Henry denied.

An unknown gentleman is heard, in passing by our *Woodhull & Claflin's Weekly* editor, Victoria, making a now often repeated claim. "I am reliably assured that Mr. Beecher preaches to at least twenty of his mistresses each Sunday."

Tilton himself, adroitly queried by Mrs. Victoria Woodhull, released to her his full masculine anguish, and gave complete corroboration of his wife's affair with their pastor and friend, Henry, and of Theodore's own wanton wanderings. His wife Elizabeth also told all to Vickie. Mrs. Woodhull, to her own mind free to love whomever she chose, had, herself, slept with the famed reverend, and romanced also, with irate, cuckolded Mr. Tilton. Mountains of evidence meticulously accumulated in the hands of our Victoria!

Lucy, Sally, Abigail, Jane, Phillis, Mary, Rebecca, Elizabeth, Anne, Shadow and I, made our way through Victoria's world and heard all we needed to hear. The pastor of Brooklyn's Plymouth Church outdid all others in this scandal. With eyes fully opened, we saw Mrs. Woodhull make her move, attacking in her *Weekly* a sexual double standard of those times. Reverend Henry Ward Beecher was exhibit number one, denier-in-chief of the day.

A century and a quarter later, in 1995, with Louisa, Victoria, Dorothea, Laura, Sarah, Margaret, and Cid all having come with, we witnessed a brilliant woman's account of both Lucy and Victoria's truth, published in *The Woman Who Ran for President*. Lois Beachy Underhill outdid her fellow historians, though some continue to this 2019 day claiming it was poor Henry Beecher who was wronged.

So now, let us hear, once more, the firsthand account of a woman who sat in a Brooklyn pew, under the sway of white male self-aggrandizing direction from he who became *The Most Famous Man in America*. Who knows what liberties Reverend Beecher may have taken the night before with any among a long list of female worshipers?

Lucy, are you ready to speak?

CHAPTER 9

Lucy

Lucy Maria Bowen (1825–1863) born Tappan

BY 2019 AT THIS FORTY-NINTH gathering, here by Pulpit Rock on another numbingly exquisite New England summer day, our eyes have been opened to once unimaginable realities. Among them, a thing called hashtags, like #MeToo and #WhyIDidntTell.

In 1863, had I not been on my deathbed, I, too, would not have told. But I was, and I did. It was only one person, my husband, who heard my truth about our pastor, the treacherous Reverend, family friend Henry Ward Beecher. We both wept, my anguished husband and I, as life slipped away; my pitiful confession to my part in lovers' deceit adding to pain beyond measure. Our ten small children, newborn to age seventeen, would soon face life without their mother.

I recall also a sudden appearance of entrancing blue eyes and the visage of a young girl with ethereal blonde hair. An angel, perhaps? But no, it is Joy and behind her, a gray-capped, white-feathered bird with gleaming gold eyes gazing my way. Girl and gull are flanked by eight faint female forms, known to me now as Anne, Elizabeth, Rebecca, Mary, Phillis, Jane, Abigail, and Sally.

In my days on earth, I, Lucy Maria Tappan, was never allowed a voice of my own; until my deathbed, that is. I lived in times, and in a family, where women were to be seen, but heard only on the domestic scene. Even there, a daughter or wife must love, honor, and obey. Men were in charge.

The youngest Tappan brothers, my Uncle Arthur and my father, Lewis, dedicated their lives to lofty goals. First, to follow in their big brother John's Boston merchant footsteps, then to carve their way into New York commerce. Second, to make use of their wealth to wage war against America's greatest sin, slavery. Third, to champion, in Calvinist spirit, the cause of keeping females in their proper place, at home and kept silent in the world of government and industry. If you do not believe me, ask Angelina Grimke.

Our congress of women, gathered again to speak at Pulpit Rock in 2019, has learned so much while traveling together through centuries of time. We see today how things have improved, it is true, for our gender. Yet of female Millennials, born early 1980s to early 2000s, now primed to replace those Baby Boomers born from 1946 to 1964, we spirits from the past must query. Does it matter first and foremost which man becomes your matrimonial match? If so, then it could be claimed that you truly are a lot like me, Lucy Tappan.

In my day, girls were valued before all else for blossoming beauty, as belles of the ball. We can safely conclude my proud father, Lewis Tappan, did not disagree with Lyman Beecher's assessment of "beautiful woman" when it came to me, Tappan's daughter. I was also a good girl who made a wonderful match, in my father's eyes, to a Tappan business partner a dozen years my senior, Henry Bowen. It has been said my portrait shows a daughter's face, both reminiscent of my delicate and charming mother, while hinting also of my father's features.

Henry was a good husband, kind it could be claimed, and more progressive than my father. Four years after our nuptials, he bought the weekly Congregationalist newspaper associated with our parish church in Brooklyn. With Pastor Henry Ward Beecher as editor, the *Independent* thrust was both anti-slavery and pro-women's suffrage. As for me, I presided over the Bowen parlor, where luminaries gathered Sundays after services at the Plymouth Church sanctuary. All the while, I kept silent about the motives and modus operandi of our sainted Reverend Beecher, until my death in 1863.

Have you dreamed of a wedding dress, I would ask of each twenty-first century female who cares to mull these matters? Mine is there for viewing in 2019 at historicnewengland.org, a testament to the age-old female role as wife and mother. I bore nine children, then died giving birth in 1863 to number ten. Back in those days, birth control was unthinkable.

So yes, times have changed, and yet remain oddly the same. Today there are churches and political parties aiming to remove birth control choices at every possible turn. But Roe v Wade still stands as law of the land. We ladies fear Kavanaugh may throw his weight around one day in the supreme halls of justice.

Meanwhile, in 2019, we view daughters of white men devoted to male power. Donald explained that a girl, like lovely, small-breasted Ivanka, could not be a "ten" on her father's scale of beauty. Next we knew, and gasped to see, a gorgeous, big-breasted woman joined her father as a valued advisor in President Trump's oval office.

Was going under the knife her answer to pressures of the day? Centuries ago, we ladies wore a bustle to enhance our behinds. We cinched our waists with corsets and plumped our bosoms with stuffing. So, we do understand bowing down to male wishes when it comes to pleasing a father desirous of a pretty little girl, or a husband whose status might well be enhanced by our striving to meet the beauty standards of our times. But still, the knife?!

Sally's paramour, Thomas Jefferson, was born into a culture of slavery and might be described as a victim of his times. My father, I have cause to believe, was in some ways also a casualty of customs of his day. My Grandmother Tappan and her fanatical Congregational evangelism guaranteed her sons' opposition to participation by females in any public forum. Uncle Arthur and my father first formed, with Garrison, the American Anti-slavery Society. Then the Tappan brothers left in protest, when Abby Kelley, a woman, was elected to the AAS business committee. A shockingly inappropriate and unacceptable step in the eyes of a Tappan family man!

Father had further seen fit to be a thorn in the side of brave Angelina Grimke, outspoken opponent to the ways of slavery so blatantly on display in her childhood home in the South. For her to speak in public to men and women alike was sin, to Lewis Tappan's evangelical mind. "Promiscuous," he called it. Angelina formed her own suffragist society, spoke far and wide on abolition and women's rights, then married fellow activist Thomas Weld.

Mr. Tappan's views were exposed in a letter to a friend who asked about Mr. Weld's, and Angelina's, ultimate disappearance from view. It has been quoted here before, and shall be again today, for entertainment of sorts. In this 2019 world, we see elitism and misogyny continue to thrive. In my day, Father showed his own hand, writing down his thoughts in 1847.

"'Where is Weld?' He is in a ditch opposite his house, doing the work any Irishman could do for 75 cents a day. His wife is 'suckling fools and chronicling small beer.'"

Who derides whom in America, we fellow travelers have made note, merely moves around the globe, as century after century goes by. The Irish then, none more than the Mexicans, it seems, right now.

Ironically, it has also been rightfully claimed that Lewis Tappan, like a black preacher we saw speak with moving power and dignity a century later at a Washington, DC mall, had a vision for centuries to come. My father dreamed that intermarriage would yield what he called a "copper-skinned" America where race would not define. Dr. Martin Luther King, Jr., spoke words heard around the world, dreaming in 1963 of his own four little children judged not by the color of their skin, but by their character. One hundred years after my death.

It seems Dr. King shared other sentiments with my own preacher, Henry Ward Beecher. Not shared with my father, Lewis Tappan, I hasten to put forth, who held marriage vows to be sacred in word and action. But to Beecher, the pastor Father helped lure to Brooklyn, lustful love, I can report firsthand, is another right of men in powerful positions. There is another right we have seen advanced, a purported privilege to endlessly deny. POTUS 45 clearly keeps this age-old tradition alive.

For me, memories of a day in 1862 come to mind. Newly with child, I suffered pangs of shame (then and now; I blush today, as I speak!) in our Plymouth Church pew, there in Brooklyn. It was our shared hypocrisy, Henry's and mine, that gave me, if not he, cause to cringe. His moving words on purity of heart, mind, and body clashed with the adulterous passion to which we had succumbed. Somehow, I believed his promise that God is Love, and our love would be blessed in the Holy Father's eyes, despite our endless lies.

On our travels through time, I suffered less to witness truth told in a book published in 1969. A century had passed. The world had so radically changed, with West Coast hippie lovers mimicking our Brooklyn ostensibly halcyon days. We noted with great interest the ending of my father's biography on page 342 which offered details of the scandal that circulated in 1873, the year of his demise. I shall quote from the second-to-last paragraph of *Lewis Tappan and the Evangelical War Against Slavery*.

"Theodore Tilton's wife had confessed to being a paramour of Henry Ward Beecher, her husband's associate on the staff of the *Independent*. Tilton, whose word on this score is still the only evidence, learned from Bowen that his wife Lucy Maria, Tappan's daughter, had also confessed to the same offense when she lay dying in 1863. While the affair did not reach the newspapers until 1873, knowledge of it traveled months before that time in the family circles involved. If Tappan ever learned of this unfortunate business, he did not record his feelings."

In 2006, we witnessed publication of Beecher's story, *The Most Famous Man in America*. Even now, nearly two centuries beyond my own 1825 birth, my truth is obscured by the faint of heart. Twenty-oh-six is a time before the "me too" era, well before "why I did not tell." Thus, biographer Debby Applegate seems to believe my husband when, at the time of Beecher's 1875 trial, Mr. Bowen denied my confession and claimed his wife had no involvement. My poor husband Henry, I can tell you, was making false accusations of libel against the *Brooklyn Argus* for "falsely" reporting my seduction.

Applegate's 2006 pointed observation that papers "reported, without evidence, that on her deathbed in 1863 Lucy Bowen had confessed to an affair with her pastor," continued a tradition of swiftly dismissing what a woman has said when a man in power is in danger of being held to account. Like Kavanaugh in 2018, Beecher, we saw on our travels, was ultimately deemed by many to be the true victim, with his accusers left reviled and disbelieved in a white-male-dominated world.

Debby Applegate did describe my husband's offers of "the love of a wife" to HWB, to get him to come to Brooklyn from Indiana. That this would become literal was certainly not my Henry's intent. Yet it did, such that the other Henry who I adored like a father would enjoy liberties with me of both adulterous and incestuous-like lechery. From 1863 onward, voyaging beyond the grave, I valued my husband's efforts to spare my children the embarrassment of their mother's, and Beecher's, true guilt.

Yet I accept also, with grateful and open heart, that the truth has a way of emerging in due time. Our compatriot, Victoria, had her own firsthand knowledge of the Brooklyn pastor's perfidy, and she had the power of the press, as well, to publish the details. Punishment of her, the messenger, came fast and furious, as she has often told and may perhaps recount again today.

Louisa may speak once more of a Boston life far from our New York fray. We have heard that literary fame for Miss Alcott allowed for travels to distant places of her times, and the chance to sample a lecture by the renowned Henry Ward Beecher. She has told before, though may not bother to repeat today, some pithy words of insight. "I was not impressed."

Soon I shall end my recollections, on our latest summer sojourn, as we wait to hear Louisa, Victoria, and more cherished voices from our collectively strengthened chorus. Before I yield, these are my final words to proffer.

We ladies have marveled in the last several years at parallels between Beecher in nineteenth-century Brooklyn, and another man of deceit, raised in Queens, who rose to the heights of U.S. power in 2016. As in the 1870s, women in the twenty-first century have emerged in droves, as a male-dominated portion of the press, led now by a fellow named Pecker, has protected a presidential political puppet from the female choir of voices. Using catch-and-kill tricks for pulp posing as news, *The National Enquirer* guaranteed innumerable indignities to our whole world at the hands of a man who would revel in his resulting role as POTUS 45.

Meanwhile, after centuries bearing witness to so many other women's lives in America, I, Lucy, am ready to offer my descendants, and the world, my own two-word truth.

Me, too.

JOY 10

I SAVOR HER GOLDEN GLOW as Lucy sheds light, for all who care to lend an ear, each time at our Pulpit Rock. A glossy chestnut brown soothes the eyes, as speaker Louisa raises her voice and salves my fears for the future of America. Forty-nine gatherings later, I find myself filled with delight at the sight and sound of each soulful spirit giving voice to her truth, one more time, on a gentle summer's day.

When Luna foretold of such females to come, my ears yearned always for more. How to open a full treasure chest of knowledge of women's lives? I would have to accept a mission to listen, learn, and then help deliver their stories to others leading busy lives of their own four centuries down the road.

"Will anyone, male or female, care to hear such history from times long before their own?"

"Yes," Luna responded and inspired, when often I raised this query. "Your sixteen ladies, time after time telling tales of old, can yield news fit to print as 2020 dawns."

"Tell me more of Louisa," I often eagerly begged. A tall girl, I had heard tell, with richly shining brown hair, who loved to go out for a run, who wished she could be as free to roam as the boys around her.

"Her father was a teacher who encouraged his pupils and his daughters to ask questions. Mr. Bronson Alcott taught through dialogue and example. Louisa shared his passion for making the world a better place."

"For people of all colors?" I prompted. Then Mother would tell again the history of the color of skin, in the world and in America. Knowledge from the future was Luna's to share, while I lay at her side and absorbed treasure troves of wisdom.

"People will learn, in the centuries to come, of the mother from whom we all descend, a shared ancestress of us all, named Lucy."

"Not Lucy Tappan. Not one of Reverend Beecher's victims," I chimed, knowing that Mother's story told of long before our fellow traveler's time.

"So long ago it is hard to measure, this other Lucy lived in the heart of the African continent, near where the earth is widest around and closest to the sun. She had gleaming dark brown skin, providing her protection from blazing rays from that giant star in the sky above."

More followed, of how Lucy's descendants yearned to wander, so they traveled both north and south, farther and farther from the earth's equator, becoming more and more pale over the vast passage of time. I soaked in details at each retelling, of those who wandered south to a land now called Australia, and those who circled north to reach what Europeans called America. Of those who went east to the vast reaches of Asia.

I heard from Luna more of our own American times, when we with pale European skin arrived to look down upon the natives, claiming our culture and our whiteness made us better than they, with their darker, red-toned complexions. And of similar denigration, based on darkness of skin, in the centuries that followed our own arrival. Vast importation from the African nations of blacks, we would call them. Once enslaved in America, they could never escape without easy identification.

That simplification became American tradition. Blacks enslaved; whites freed. Black was lesser; white was better. Blacks were not allowed to learn their letters. Like white females denied an education, blacks remained confined in their fetters.

"Then Bronson Alcott took exception!" I whispered in unison with Luna, as she reached this part of her story. I loved to hear how Louisa and her family played a small part in the wide-ranging effort called the underground railroad. How abolitionists like Lucy's father would take the side of the "darkies" to bring them freedom from their chains.

Certainly, more freedom for girls like Louisa would follow!

"Your own story, too, my dear Joy, will serve to inform."

My scalp sometimes tingled as Mother provoked a deep desire to join forces, over four centuries, with females like me who suffered the indignities of subjugation in a world of white male-dominated systems.

Hearing Lucy speak again today, under this glorious August sun, leaves me basking in a glow, then eager for Louisa's glossy chestnut aura, when she stands to speak once more.

More of my own tale can certainly wait. Let us hear straight away now, from our famed, dare I say widely misunderstood, author of *Little Women*.

CHAPTER 10

Louisa

Louisa May Alcott (1832–1888) cradle to grave

I NEVER MARRIED. I NEVER gave birth. I preserved my freedom. I had a voice.

Each time we pause this excursion through the years, raising our voices here at Pulpit Rock, I have compared myself in this way to those who came before me. Anne, Elizabeth, Rebecca, Mary, Phillis, Jane, Abigail, Sally, and Lucy have all understood: I mean no disrespect. Mating, producing an average of eight children each, was the right choice, often the only choice, for females in their day.

Yet when Joy, Shadow, and followers found Lucy in her 1863 birth-room deathbed, urging her to "come with" and see how the world "gets better," it is my story, in part, which serves to explain.

Spinsterhood, as my status has so often been called, was no scourge for me. The benefits were many and the pitfalls few. A life of perpetual abstinence from perhaps life's greatest passion -- the joy of sex -- is in no way required of those who, like me, choose to never marry, never have children. Thank heavens! Truth be told, sex is fun.

On this 2019 transcendent summer day, warm breezes bring back sense memories from spring travels on the European continent when I, too, felt free to indulge. I chuckle on this posthumous journey with fellow ladies as my friend Julian, hallowed Hawthorne's son, remembers me thus. "Did she ever have a love affair? We never knew; yet how could such a nature so imaginative, romantic, and passionate escape it?"

I have more than once, when taking this annual turn to tell my tale, seen fit to concur. I'm long gone from the gravitational pull of mother earth, after all. Modesty, decorum and such, they no longer require complete silence on this matter. My 1865 Paris journal entry, casually mentioned a time or two, does begin, "A little romance with Laddie." Some here have observed a misty tinge to my chestnut tone, when I read aloud a notation from May 1866: "on the 17th reluctantly left for London."

Yet no woman in Massachusetts, in my day, would have publicly proclaimed those words, "sex is fun!" My Boston world, unlike Victoria's New York surroundings or even Lucy's in Brooklyn, was far too protected to allow trumpeting of such truth. My sensual voice, to be found in my romantic pulp fiction, would be published under pseudonym's cloak.

In 2019, the world best knows me, Louisa May Alcott, as the author of the 1868 novel, *Little Women.* I had thirty-six years of life on earth behind me, twenty more left to be lived, when my publisher launched my most famous work. Wikipedia tells its version of me, a female born November 29, 1832, in Germantown, Pennsylvania. Now, for nearly half-a-century, I have spoken for myself, each year here at the Rock.

That I could, among those of us on this voyage be first to forgo marriage and children, followed closely from another benefit none before my time shared. A father, both famed and infamous in his teaching days, who would expose his four daughters to Boston's elite world of intellectuals, forming fast friendships with writers whose power of the pen created a Transcendental movement still revered to this day. At each annual gathering here by a glacial monument, I take joy in my memories of those who were my mentors.

My own early passion for putting prose to parchment blossomed in Concord, twenty miles northwest of Harvard Yard, where Mr. Emerson and Mr. Thoreau had the benefit of education reserved for males only. Margaret Fuller joined our ranks, a female inspiration adding to daily intellectual feasts. My self-educated father, urged by Waldo, as his peers called him, first brought my mother, my sisters, and me to this Concord haven when I was a wide-eyed child of eight years. We stayed there for three years, then went elsewhere on Father's search for a path through life. Soon, to my delight, we returned to plant roots at Hillside, back in Concord throughout my teenage angst.

Thus, I could soak up wonders of Walden Pond, with Mr. Thoreau pointing, explaining, and patiently answering girlish queries about Nature and her mysteries. In his *Civil Disobedience*, or *Resistance to Civil Government*, a first chosen title, we saw how Father's abolitionist ideas and example had inspired my kindly teacher to expound. We must not let Presidents Polk or Taylor make us agents of injustice, was the word about Concord town. Now in 2019, we excursionists see rampant remnants of race inequality still require those of conscience to make their raised voices heard.

In four-hundred-year-old America, it is clear to we who have navigated the centuries, gender equality continues to lag in the wake of matters of race. Sadly, neither has nearly resolved in 2019. For me, Civil War years melded a mix of eye-opening realities. A woman's role was to serve as cook, seamstress or nurse, as the fight to free blacks from slavery met a Southern white-skinned fury. The men in charge were willing to butcher our young boys in most bountiful numbers.

I, who always begrudged my female status as "lady," while lads got to be "lord of creation," contrived to go to Washington, DC, and learned to nurse those boys who I could not be. A huge, blonde Virginia blacksmith lived less than two days in my care. My *Hospital Sketches* tells the tale for those who were not there. For me, even now, early wartime memories take me back in an instant's time to the final moments for that gentle John.

His eyes gazed sweetly upon me, poor substitute for mother, wife or sister though I be. "I guess I'm moving on, ma'am?" this bravest man among my forty softly asked. "You'd better tell him," a brusque, hardened doctor had warned. Thus, "I'm afraid so," was my sad reply. As for John, he never spoke again.

Yet my touch seemed to soothe, so to the end, he held my hand closely. Soon a grey veil fell that no human hand could lift, and I saw the face of someone no longer here. Yet John's grip did not let me draw my hand away until, at last, he was made by the living to loosen. Four white marks remained across the back of my own appendage, even when warmth and color returned -- a reminder of men who must give their lives, while females sit on the sidelines of a world with only men in charge.

As an army nurse, age thirty, I'd claimed my spinster status, declared myself a "woman's rights woman." Irreverent, as well, when I visited the Senate chamber on evening wanderings; I sat right in Sumner's chair. I went where I wanted and did as I liked.

Even more a happy spinster in 1868, as creator of *Little Women,* I determinedly resisted the pressures to marry my character, Jo, to her wealthy suitor, Laurie. Sister Amy would rise to a bride's role, all pretty and ready to please. Jo, for the meantime, remained more like myself, dearly attached, thank you kindly, to my independence.

The method to my madness, as my audacious female grasp for freedom might be viewed, may more graciously be written up as Emersonian self-reliance. We have seen, and may hear again today, how fellow voyager Dorothea, sharp of tongue like me, and full of cutting phrases for the ages, urged the twentieth-century world to *Wake Up and Live!* In 2019, we now note, a Kindle offering of said work proclaims Dorothea's Emersonian-like urgings to be, "One of the greatest self-help books ever written."

I succumbed soon enough in my nineteenth-century fight to forestall matrimony in fiction. Girls wrote and begged long and hard. So, I did marry Jo off, but to a kindly old professor, in *Little Men,* to run a school for boys. Then, yes, have babies of their own, delivering that yearned for, so oft-manufactured, happily ever after. Our real-life Alcott family would move out of debt, become moderately well-to-do, thus making my literary accommodations, to my mind, quite worthwhile.

For me, adventures, free and unencumbered, kept calling. The Civil War years had been my first opportunity; it ended with my battle with typhoid, but not before dissection of a body had been offered for my curious viewing. To this day, I know not just why I declined. Cid tells with panache, on occasion by our Pulpit, of doing the honors herself, in medical school days. "I did dissect a man," became her crowning credential, earning admission to an otherwise all-male adventure on the Colorado River.

Cid had grandchildren at the time of her river-rafting, adventurous days, so that "Whish! There goes grandmother," is the title and topic of a full chapter in her memoir. As for me, I recall among my own adventures a rather brief but sweet dive into the realm of motherhood, the last decade of my life.

My littlest sister, May, a talented artist among the Paris crowd, you know, had met and married a Swiss fellow. A sad ending transpired for her in 1879, just weeks after the birth of a first child, reminiscent of our fellow traveler Lucy's passing, at the birth of her tenth. May's child, Lulu, for a few short years, became my beloved daughter, until I, too, joined Joy's gaggle in 1888.

Upon my death, the father of my "child" finally insisted on the return of Louisa May Nieriker to Switzerland, at the tender age of nine. For hints of her life with me, I suggest a glance or two at my 1885 book of children's stories, *Lulu's Library*. My own fondest mother-daughter memories are of one 1884 Massachusetts summer sojourn on Narragansett Bay in Nonquitt, with happy child-staged theatre productions reminiscent of my own youth. Harriet Reisen's 2009 biography can tell you more about both me and Lulu.

Now with Cid and our fellows, on spirited posthumous shenanigans through time, I champion Joy's vision, learned at Luna's knee. The seats in DC chambers, there on Capitol Hill, must be equal in gender. I recall my small satisfaction in 1862, seated in poor old Sumner's Senate chair. Much was murky in those Civil War years. Our sight began to clear a century and half down history's wild and rocky road.

A sea change, a full paradigm shift, is well overdue. Time for women, men too, as Dorothea might turn a phrase, to wake themselves to a new level of living. Liberate America from patriarchal chains. Forgo the urge to turn wholly matriarchal. Rise to new heights with a government guarantee of perfectly equal gender representation.

Fifty-fifty, our twenty-twenty message boldly bawls.

This is our more perfect union.

My soap box shivers underfoot as I speak, calling out, "Louisa, it is time to pause." Victoria will soon, once again, indubitably leave us in awe. "Rest your jaws," my platform urges. "Shake yourself loose, to let Joy have her next say."

JOY 11

"WHY A QUEEN, WHEN YOU were born, but no king?"

A favorite tale, among those I begged Luna to tell, was the story of life on earth in 1600, the year Mother said she was born. She would never speak of her parentage, which remains mysterious to this day.

"Queen Elizabeth had been on her throne forty-two years," Mother would say of the English monarch. "You have seen how our widow Elizabeth Warren has not remarried and so remains in charge of herself and family. The Queen of England, in power also at the time of our Elizabeth Walker Warren's birth, never married at all. She was known as the virgin queen. Perhaps this explains those many decades of successful rule."

My child's mind felt like a fire, thirsting for signs that the world could birth true equality for girls. "When there was an English queen, for all those long years, could others of her same sex do all that men do?"

Chuckles from Luna followed, then more stories of kings, queens, battles, beheadings, machinations, and short or long wars followed by uneasy, always temporary, peace. A beheading story Mother told, the one stuck permanently in my own head, was of the mother of Elizabeth I, when the future queen was a toddler two years of age.

"Princess Elizabeth's father, King Henry the Eighth, wanted a son, which the little girl's mother, Anne Boleyn, could not produce. When planning Anne's beheading, to pave way for remarriage, Henry's act of mercy was to order use of a sword, not an axe, for a swifter, less gruesome end. He and Jane Seymour were wed ten days after."

"The longest British reigns, from the time of my birth until the time of your 2020 message, should you choose to deliver it, will be those of three strong women." I learned that Elizabeth I died when Mother was three, ending her rule of near forty-five years.

Luna knew, and told, that an even longer female reign would commence two centuries beyond Mother's upcoming passing. In 1837, Victoria would ascend the throne to cries of "Long live the Queen." And live long she would, until 1901, completing sixty-four years total, nearly two decades more than Elizabeth I before her.

Another half century forward, in 1952 as Luna foretold, Queen Elizabeth II would become the next female monarch of England. "In 2019, my child, you will still be able to view QE II celebrating, with pomp and circumstance, as children and grandchildren marry and give birth to future royalty. She will have reached her sixty-seventh year on the throne, outdoing even Queen Victoria."

"More, please, more!" I begged.

"Look for Prince Harry's wife, Meghan Markle, a woman of color and of American birth, newly titled Duchess of Sussex. She will proudly proclaim herself a feminist. Her passions will include gender equality."

"About time," I responded with glee, when gifted by Mother with this long-awaited gem.

"In between?" I then queried, eager to return to tales of American women in centuries to come.

"No kings or queens for the land where you were born, dear Joy," Luna oft assured. "Seeds of democracy, with a voice for men like Masters Alden, Warren, Winslow, and others, would be sown by their body politic."

"With no women, no women deemed fit to sign," my girlish resentments each time had me cry. A squeak, then a squeal, as I heard my words rise, choking my throat to then silence my cries.

"There, there, I have more to tell. Times will change and move toward justice. Let me soothe you with stories. Put your head on my shoulder and listen a spell."

"Will we vote, will we lead, will we gain equal power?" I sobbed as I asked, fearing even Luna could not truly make such a promise. In Plymouth, all seemed hopeless after that demeaning disaster on the Duxburrow Trail.

But there was hope, after all, for women to join a body politic, and find freedom for our gender equal to the males. Luna's promise cautioned, "Slowly. Slow pace at first. But ever more swiftly, females join males to lift the curse."

Fellow voyager, Victoria, was soon a topic from Mother's treasure chest of knowledge. In a frontier Ohio town less than fifty miles south of Lake Erie, Victoria was born in 1838, one year after a teen-aged queen's ascension. Mother explained that was the reason for the given name chosen for this beautiful baby girl. A glorious rainbow glow appeared before my closed eyes, while I listened to the tale of Victoria Claflin's life, as told by Luna.

Since our annual gatherings began in 1971, what fabulous stories our eleventh wandering spirit has had to tell. No crystal prism, pierced through by the sun's rays, ever yielded a more beauteous rainbow than Victoria.

Will you treat us now, fellow traveler, to more?

CHAPTER 11

Victoria

Victoria California Woodhull (1838–1927) born Claflin

"I AM A PROPHETESS," I claimed in 1871. "I am an evangel." "I am a Savior, if you would but see it." My words. My weekly paper. My nineteenth-century mission.

I rarely published editorials in the *Weekly* under my own byline. But exposing Henry Ward Beecher, along with our eternally hypocritical institutions designed to elevate males at women's expense? My status, with sister Tennie, as the first famed females to own and publish a prominent newspaper, required that I rise to that challenge. It appeared no one else was willing or able to do so.

I was also the first woman financier to broker her own fortune on Wall Street, having set up household in New York City on the north side of East 38th, between Fifth and Madison Avenues. There, a wealthy woman could live life on her own terms, right along with wealthy men of the times.

My sister's romance with Commander Cornelius Vanderbilt paved our way. We called our firm, Woodhull, Claflin & Co. Our power of the purse led to power of the press, by way of *Woodhull & Claflin's Weekly*.

"I believe it is my duty and mission to carry the torch to light up and destroy the heap of rottenness which, in the name of religion, marital sanctity, and social purity, now passes as the social system." What personal history brought me to publish this profound understanding?

Today, Louisa has reminded that, back in 1888, all who welcomed her to our navigation through time had averaged more than eight births. She was our first to never marry, never give birth.

I, the next to join this excursion in 1927, was our first to divorce. Ultimately, I could and did avail of that opportunity not once, but twice. And yes, I married a third and final time, happy at last. It was a long, long road from Homer, Ohio, to my last days living in an English manor.

"I was near fourteen when I married," I told the world, by way of a letter printed in 1875 in that very same *Weekly*. How so? As I speak those words this moment, in the warm rainbow of sunrays at Pulpit Rock, the year, for me, becomes 1853. My setting is Cuyahoga County, Ohio, at my birthplace, Homer. It is a mere two months after my fifteenth birthday, as Dr. Woodhull and I wed.

Why did I so choose? Did I have a choice? Yes? No? Hardly?

My first fourteen years were spent close by my mother's side, absorbing the powers of prophecy and learning to heal, better than most physicians of the day. Thus, I made my first fortune. Then I wed.

I soon learned Dr. Canning Woodhull was an alcoholic womanizer. He was also father to my only offspring, darling Zula and poor Byron. Neither would ever have children of their own. Moving on from their father, I married again to Colonel Blood, the year 1866, in nearby Montgomery. With my sister, Tennessee, in tow, we were set to storm New York City, financial center of the world.

Hypocrisy. It was the hypocrisy of Henry Ward Beecher which galled the most. I am a woman, with multiple momentous life memories. Chaos, some would say. Progress, I claim. By joining a male world and adopting their style of sleeping with whomever appealed, I was perfectly positioned to foment change.

After all, I, too, had shared extramarital moments of passion with Henry. I, too, heard, from the lips of both Tiltons, sad stories of vows betrayed. Bowen told Tilton, who told me, of Lucy's pained deathbed confession.

My *Weekly* allowed me to make public the secrets of our world, adding a female instinct to be forthcoming and truthful, and overcoming a pervasive hypocrisy shared by the Tiltons, Beechers, and Bowens of the day. We, on our travels in 2019, see a forthright Stormy Daniels, and a long list more of females speaking truth to power, filling publications with antidotes to pervasive lies told by Trumps, Epsteins, and Cosbys.

My 1870s prophecies about the future of marriage, female suffrage, and who would ultimately seize control? My twenty-first century eye allows me to see the error of those earlier days. A swing of the pendulum, from men in charge to women in charge, was a rash prediction. It took my 1927 departure from mortal existence, with that visit from Joy, Shadow, Anne, Elizabeth, Rebecca, Mary, Phillis, Jane, Abigail, Sally, Lucy, and Louisa, to allow for adventures into a world where gender equal government could ultimately provide safe and healthy middle ground.

All those endless ghastly tales, like Lucy's sad story of a powerful predatory preacher; Elizabeth Tilton's wrecked life at the hands of the same greedy Henry Ward Beecher; Jane Doe's pitiful plight at age thirteen, there in Harvey Epstein's New York City mansion, she "too afraid to show her face" in 2016; and Ms. Daniels' boldly revealed reality of Trump travesties, each stems from a world with no true system of gender equality. Men maintain their longstanding death grip on power, in entertainment and in industry, all supported by a Constitution which fails to grant representational equality to women in our beloved American government. Abigail wrote truly to John. Such tyranny would not, could not sustain.

Yet even 1920's long overdue female-vote-granting Nineteenth Amendment failed to achieve our rightful status. Yes, in the twentieth century women gained recognition as true citizens in the government's eyes. We have the right to vote. Yet we have seen in the century since, equal representation is yet to come. Institutionalized fifty-fifty representation is the next worthy goal. That twenty-first century mission I now share with you ladies gathered here on this blessed August day.

Many a time on this gorgeous island, you have heard me tell that old story of a female fight for citizen status. My 1872 appeal to Grant, in his oval office, to support our Sixteenth Amendment franchising women was met with a patronizing pat on the head. That final effort to achieve success for a long-fought mission would fail. Our female plea for equity was buried in Committee, never again to see the light of day, serving only as added inspiration. So much had transpired prior. So, if you will, suffer me to digress.

As the archives do still prove, my November 19, 1871, edition of *Woodhull & Claflin's Weekly*, had provided my readers with publication of the Constitution in full. By that very document's definition, "All persons born or naturalized" in our great country "are citizens." Make note, I argued, that our founding fathers never used the terms "man" or "woman." "Persons" includes females; thus, women are citizens entitled to vote. "I do now proclaim to the women of the United States of America that they are enfranchised," I hastened to make clear.

Soon a female "first" came to pass, back in Washington, DC, one Thursday in January 1872. A Congressional Judiciary Committee, never before having deigned to openly hear a woman speak to their august body, held just such a hearing. I presented my case. It is true that at first my voice quavered, but then it grew bold and strong.

"Women constitute a majority of this country – they hold vast portions of the nation's wealth and pay a proportionate share of the taxes. They are entrusted with the most vital responsibilities of society; they bear, rear and educate men; they train and mold their characters; they inspire the noblest impulses in men; they often hold the accumulated fortunes of a man's life for the safety of the family and as guardians of the infants, and yet they are debarred from uttering any opinion by public vote."

Now the time had come. It is reserved, I urged, "for America to sweep away the mist of prejudice and ignorance, and that chivalrous condescension of a darker age," ending with prayerful exhortation that "the wisdom of Congress may be moved to action in this matter."

I was praised near and far, acclaimed at the Women's Suffrage Convention next door, yet Congress was in no way so moved. Thus, my nomination, by the Equal Rights Party, as their 1872 candidate for President of the United States. I shall not re-tell today that whole tale. Lois Underhill succeeded in superb fashion in 1995 with *The Woman Who Ran for President*.

I returned from England in 1892, to try once more. I need not tell the world that neither effort would succeed. Grant retained his power, in 1872. Two decades later, Cleveland scoffed at such futile female challenges. Even in 2016, we see the concept of a female President of the United States of America was met with monstrous male scorn, derision, and a successful worldwide conspiracy to obstruct any such upset to male-dominated systems in America.

What about that third marriage, in 1883, to a wealthy British banker, which led to a softening of my views? My belief in "free love" would modify to a version preferred by many, even in 2019. Rather than separating sex from marriage, rather than prioritizing women's consent and pleasure, my emphasis became simply the choice to leave an unbearable marriage. As nineteenth century turned to twentieth, I came to accept the protection marriage could afford a woman who once fought hard and long against such masculine institutions. Someday there would be no need. For me, in my day, it became a necessity.

It was time to work from within, and a widely read publication, the *Humanitarian*, was my new voice from England. I had a daughter, you ladies may recall, who worked at my side as my own mother had done. There was safety for my son Byron, as well, in this proper British world, with me now Mrs. John Biddulph Martin. Fault me, if you will, but those days of my life yielded fulsome fond memories and added balance to tales of bitter battles back in the States.

I do not think I am an enigma to those who care to listen, read, and learn. Ask of Isabella Beecher Hooker, the sister of Lucy's preacher nemesis, "What were *your* impressions?" Perhaps Mrs. Hooker will repeat her many kind words about me, first offered in 1872.

"Heaven sent for the rescue of woman from her pit of subjection," "less a woman than an embodiment of pure thought, soul and reason," and even "a prophetess, full of visions and messages to the people which it would be woe unto her to refrain from proclaiming, even if martyrdom were sure to follow." On the latter, my motives, I remain eternally grateful to Henry Ward Beecher's gentle sibling, for her opining.

Others, then and now, may be moved to disagree. Yet in the nineteenth-century eyes of fellow female advocate, Isabella, I was an "idealist – a visionary perhaps – but she is without consciousness of self and absolutely without selfishness. Her standard of benevolence is unapproachable to most of us – and she has lived up to it."

May I, and all gathered here, soon live up to Joy's 2020 challenge. May we bravely deliver, midst desperate times, a message of groundbreaking hope for this world. My fellow nineteenth-century suffragists lost the Sixteenth Amendment fight. Three amendments later, valiant twentieth-century women won their battle for the Nineteenth.

This twenty-first-century world, led by a Congress reviled more than an infestation of the cockroach, wants only for truth spoken to power. We see Alexandria Ocasio-Cortez bravely making bold, principled progress. When her female fellows in government rise to numbers equal to men, no more and no less, a long list of injustices will be put to rest.

In truth, power must be shared by both genders, in equal measure. The world's greatest government must now rise to the greatest level of all. Amend our Constitution is our clarion call.

Toward that end, I rest my case today, and yield back to our leader. All the sooner to hear from Dorothea, Laura, Sarah, Margaret, and Cid.

JOY 12

AH, VICTORIA, WE SAVOR YOUR tales of a life well lived, a rare woman in the foreground of what could only be termed "a man's world." With fortitude and valor, you forged a way forward for all. Each gathering time, as you take your turn to speak, I return to childhood feelings, centuries prior, when my own female resentments simmered or came to full boil.

I had Luna, and her wisdom, to sometimes soothe.

"Yes," Mother agreed often, "It is not fair that girls must remain silent, while boys have their say. Nor is it right, or just, that change will come at a near glacial pace, seemingly as slow as the migration of Clark's Island's mammoth rock to her final resting place on the isle of your birth."

"Why?" was my frequent girlish reply.

"Reasons are many, dear child. Think a while, about this. Throughout the millennia, men's size has meant males take charge. Yet greater height and strength have only come to them after long years of childhood, at their mother's knee. As masculine fury builds, many boys enter manhood with resentments of their own, not much different from yours."

"But their fathers, and their mothers, have let them do more than the girls, even while no difference in size!" I complained.

"True, my Joy, but still, sad to say, male fury oft has no bounds. You shall see, should you travel forward through centuries' time, continued travesties, with higher and higher depths of destruction, of self and others."

Once more, Luna's words called to my mind stories of ghastly wars, with women waiting at the sidelines, sewing flags and watching over the wounded until the grey veil that no human hand can lift falls again over another dying man's face. Louisa, as Mother foretold, was among those ladies watching.

"Women will lead the way to a world without endless war. Your message, if and when delivered, will pave a path. Both women and men in charge, in equal numbers, is not an instant fix to this world's woes, but a necessary step to rid humanity of the monstrous imbalance imposed when only men are in charge."

"Yes!" I exclaimed. "We females should share equally in deciding matters of justice." Mother told me then of a prophecy by a man of the future, both famed and infamous, as Lucy has today made note.

"As Dr. King will proclaim to a twentieth-century world, the moral arc of the universe bends toward justice."

What a long wait there would be. As a child, waiting for change could seem like forever. Yet sometimes, before I knew it, there Luna and I were, doing new things with new people in someplace new.

While Plymouth's Hobb's Hole was home to Mother and me, with Widow Warren mistress of the place and Nathaniel my favorite charge, Priscilla and John Alden were busy building on land in Duxburrow. By 1629, a summer home for the growing season was complete. There, eldest child Elizabeth, youngest girl Sarah, with boys in the middle John and Joseph, could shelter and play, as their parents farmed their parcel of 120 acres.

We travelers have visited another old Alden foundation, behind the 2019 Duxbury Schools complex. Ten-and-a-half feet long by thirty-eight feet wide. Bits of brick-red pottery have been garnered, we learned, by fascinated students of that American archaeological treasure. Thunderstorms had cleared the air, that first Sunday this past June. A short walk down the nearby damp path, we gazed in admiration at a Duxbury delight. A fully preserved dwelling, built in the

1670s, had made room for the Alden clan onward through the centuries. First owned, we are told, by Ruth's brother, Jonathan.

There we hovered where aging John and Priscilla once tread. We marveled at centuries-old spinning wheels by the ancient brick hearth, at bedsteads, bureaus, and floorboards where, through long generations, offspring set foot for gatherings of their own in the winter, spring, summer, or fall. Glancing through glass pane windows, we looked down upon beautiful barn-red bricks, added annually to the patio and walkway, with tributes to descendants and celebrators of those eye-opening, priceless memories.

By the mid-1630s, that old foundation site, up the way, had become a year-round home to all, including Luna and me. My new favorite, Ruth, had come into the world in 1634, following the 1632 arrival of brother Jonathan. By 1638, another babe was on the way.

Back in 1632, the Standish family had made their permanent home in Duxbury with little Alexander, Lora, and Myles junior in tow. Father Myles and mother Barbara farmed their acres on Standish Shore, a few miles south of our Alden lands, with native Hobbamock a treasured member of their household. By 1638, old foot paths had been broadened to make the Duxburrow Trail, allowing for wagon travel in just the right direction. Hitching up the oxcart for a visit, with views of Duxbury-Plymouth Bay and of Clark's Island, brought smiles to all our faces.

Josiah had been added in 1633 to the Standish family crew, just one year older than four-year-old Ruth Alden, and Charles in 1635, he one year younger than my favorite girl. Myles and Barbara's eldest, Alexander, was three years older than Sarah Alden, Alex aged fourteen to her eleven. Sarah loved to play with Lora, her exact same age, yet the eldest Standish boy was clearly a favorite, even then.

Sitting on warm beige sands, gazing over glistening blue waters toward long white stretches of beach bordering Plymouth Harbor, I cherished snatched freedom from cares, as I basked in the sun, dreaming of even better days to come. In that moment, I pondered over Mother's words. "Sarah will one day marry Captain Standish's eldest, Alexander. Ruth will marry a man from Braintree, John Bass. But you, my Joy, should you choose, can witness all that and so much more, with intriguing women through four centuries time, in order to deliver a 2020 message."

That might mean no reveling in the touch of Thomas Southworth. But think of four hundred years of annual return to these beautiful bays, to that gorgeous island nestled in the arms of golden beaches, while traveling around a great growing country between visits! A chance to see things get better, after inevitable trials and tribulations? I remember a growing warmth in my heart, matching the comfort of my feet cradled in warm sand, as my choice grew ever more certain.

Thus, here we now stand, near four centuries later, on a majestic summer's day, by an ancient rock on revered Clark's Island, hearing a long list of life stories. Abigail, as Luna whispered ages ago in my girlish ear, would wed a descendant of Ruth Alden. He, from the Adams clan, was destined to be a second President for a United States of America. One of many reasons, we have learned, John and Priscilla's child was placed in my constant care. John Adams would trust his wife's guidance, often but not always.

"Will I meet *Mayflower* descendants, if I choose to journey through time?" I eagerly asked Mother as a girl. What a magical adventure, it seemed that would be.

"Ah, yes," came the welcome reply. "Three of your favorites from my stories, who might join you on such travels, harken back to these days."

And as we have since heard tell at these annual reunions, our next fellow voyager, Dorothea, is the first multiple-lined member of our *Mayflower* triad. She, like Abigail's husband, a testament to an eagle-eyed watch over Ruth, when that girl was in my care. Second, Laura -- proof that dedication to Nathaniel, my favorite Warren charge, would move the world onward and upward, through centuries' time. Laura, seventh cousin to Dorothea, shares Richard Warren descent. Third, our Sarah, sharing the White line with Dorothea; seventh cousins also, those two.

Alice Dorothea Alden Thompson, famed as editor and author Dorothea Brande, could meet cousins Laura and Sarah. Laura Elizabeth Ingalls, renowned as writer and author Laura Ingalls Wilder, could meet cousin Dorothea and fellow *Mayflower* descendant Sarah. Sarah Wingate Taylor, treasured teacher, writer, poet, Clark's Island owner, could meet cousin Dorothea and fellow descendant, Laura. All celebrate Sarah as Clark's property donor, so that Duxbury town and her Historical Society could become careful preservers of this land under our feet, my place of birth.

Each such fellow traveler holds shared knowledge of American ancestry, ancient and recent, with priceless meaning for women and men of 2020 and beyond. Let us hear, now, from the first of our three, Dorothea!

CHAPTER 12

Dorothea

Dorothea Alden Brande (1893–1948) born Thompson

"KINDLE?!" "PRICELESS!" ONE OF YOU fellow voyagers marveled at the gate, just weeks after our annual Clark's Island congress in 2001. Boston Logan was mere minutes, as the crow flies, from the room at renowned Massachusetts General Hospital where I had joined our 1948 gaggle, fifty-three years prior to this airport meeting. It was now September 11, 2001.

"Why?" I wondered. Why did Joy lead us to this moment on our centuries-long journey?

The United boarding line moved slowly as tickets were handed to agents smoothly, one by one. Suddenly, a startled passenger pivoted and returned with speed to a recently exited waiting spot. There it was, still safe in a black and silver seat, ready to be retrieved. That little girl's Kindle.

"Is this what we were meant to see?" I reflected. This miracle of modern devices, where books like Laura's, and mine, Margaret's and Cid's, midst many million others, are viewed with ease, so lightly carried anywhere on earth?

Might this magic be part and parcel of our mission, bringing a priceless message to a twenty-first-century world? A call, to women and men alike, exclaiming *Wake Up and Live!*? A challenge to enter the land of GEG?

Yes, we ladies joined Joy and Shadow that day, when wheels lifted from tarmac, and United flight 175 left the lovely greens and blues of Boston and her historic harbor behind. Again, we followed alongside the invention called airplane, fueled by a substance called gasoline. Then we viewed, in horror, the New York City streets below, a World Trade Center Tower straight ahead, with no chance to escape the deafening sound and deadly impact. Nothing left but to pick up the pieces. So many souls. A small child's Kindle.

Because Ted Doty survived a near-shipwreck on Clark's Island shore, I am here. Ted weathered also the winter of 1620-21, as did the *Mayflower*'s John Alden, ship's cooper, as did Priscilla Mullins, girl of his dreams and daughter of deceased shoemaker William and wife Alice. All my ancestors, and thus, I am here. Ship-born baby Peregrine White and widowed mother, Susanna, were survivors also. Because of many prolific progeny-producing matrimonial matches that followed, lo, I am here to tell of my own 1892 birth.

This would not be, if Ted Doty or any named other, had perished. Yet here I stand, set to tell, as best I can, all that we ladies have heard and seen to follow.

Long after I was gone, my boy, Gilbert, we heard tell on our travels, recalled my claims to *Mayflower* ancestry. I had a short nine years to kindle curiosity in the mind of my precious charge, child of Seward Collins. By marriage time for my eldest boy, Justin Brande, only Sewie and nine-year-old Gil could attend the New Hampshire wedding. My youngest had last viewed me through a New Hampshire hospital window, exchanging wave of hand while awaiting the outcome of my illness.

When my time had come, that same 1948 year, and my last moments approached in a private room at famed Massachusetts

General, it was Joy who came to call. With her, eleven other female spirits from our American past hovered, while heart slowed in my mortal breast. Gilbert, to my dread, must make do without his mother. I had done all I could do, in a struggling twentieth-century world.

Blue eyes peered into my soul, as an angelic voice soothed, "It gets better." "I want to see," I heard myself reply.

"Rise, and come with," a whole chorus called.

And so, I did just that, eight days before Gilbert's ninth Christmas.

And now, this fine August day, at the forty-ninth reunion by age-old Pulpit Rock, I find myself eager as a young girl. There is magic in writing, my seven-year-old self discovered. Down that path I hurtled, with hardly a waiver. I had lived life informed by centuries-long heritage. I have witnessed the meaning of Joy's Luna-inspired message. Finally, today, I shall truly add my say.

From my maternal side, old Alden tales came handed down. And this moment, as I speak, my mother's passing fills my heart and mind. I see myself as such a very young girl in June 1908 when, oh, yes, I did weep. No sweetness at all, when at sixteen, my momma was gone forever to her grave.

Like Priscilla, before me, a mother's passage left a pall. Yet my ancestress lost not only her mother, but also her father and her brother mere months following their Atlantic crossing after leaving all other kin behind. Surely that springtime was a most painful one for that Mullins sole survivor. Centuries ago, at the same age as I, a young girl in her teens, Prissy was left orphaned, feeling ever so deeply alone.

What worlds of difference, in my day, from that *Mayflower* winter and spring. I had, still, my father, brother, and many older sisters. What's more, in my times, education could be had by an ambitious Midwestern girl in the state of Illinois. Chicago had the skyscraper, the department store, a female work force, and unfettered capitalism. Also, a mighty university, on Lake Michigan shores.

Priscilla and John's daughter, Ruth, from whom I proudly descend, was kept from the childhood schoolhouse by culture's patriarchal bent.

Scratching scant home-learned letters in mudflats, while in Joy's charge, left all else beyond reach for a girl in Ruth Alden's era. My cousin John, Ruth's famed Adams offspring of male descent? In 1776, he remained paternalistically consistent. "Depend upon it, we know better than to repeal our Masculine Systems," John Adams insisted.

To "It gets better," Joy's signature line, my teenage years gave meaning, perhaps my listeners will find. Though it was daunting at first to penetrate all-male institutions, hordes of female ascenders stormed the walls of the University of Chicago castle. I received freshman honors in 1912, on the *Kalailu* rolls, amongst fifty brave young women with status in that stormer society. In the end, I would be Phi Beta Kappa, with University of Michigan another alma mater.

I, "Dorothea Thompson," could not vote, but with persistence and determination, education challenges were conquered, and I wrote. Oh, yes, I wrote. And the Chicago Tribune, lo and behold, would have me as a female reporter.

Virgin Miss Anthony, revered women's vote advocate, in the fashion of England's virgin queen Elizabeth, had long held her American throne as Suffragist Queen. At a birthday celebration, just days before her passing, consecration to the cause had left SBA certain. "Failure is impossible," she proclaimed. Then, as had Elizabeth I in 1603, our never-married, eighty-six-year-old Susan, went chastely to her 1906 grave.

But for me, one decade after, a temptation, by the name of Brande, would exert inexorable power.

War threatened in Europe, meaning America's men soon would be seen off by weeping war brides, countrywide. Yet what a whole new world in the year 1916. There, in female martial service, I was proudly announced on August 24 as wed to Herbert Brande. Our trusted Tribune headlined, "First War Bridegroom." My prior title, "Alice Dorothea Alden Thompson," now was dutifully replaced with the moniker Dorothea Brande.

116

You see, fellow history viewers, Wisconsin Woman's Military Training was mostly a passing fancy. Writing was my passion, and Herbert's too. "Newspaper man," for "Chicago Tribune" was entered on his June 5, 1917, draft registration. With baby Justin having arrived May 30, 1917, the dependents listed showed as "wife and child." I, truth be told, also was a journalist, a reporter; thus, careers would continue, for both husband and his bride.

Nineteen-twenty saw us U.S. Census listed, still with the Trib, with the separate status for me as mere "writer," while the man of the family was known for "Editorial" glib. Mister Brande is elsewhere cited, another truth be told, as being on, or off, the wagon. Nonetheless, by 1922, the Brandes left Chicago behind and Bermuda travels brought us home to big, bustling New York City.

By 1925, the census taker found us on West 68th, husband and wife both listed as "writer" (Herbert was demoted), with eight-year-old Justin "at school."

Anthony's passion for Temperance relates, sadly, to this tale. By 1930, East 19th is my home; a single woman, a single mother of a twelve-year-old child. Yet, "Editor" I can proudly state, to the census taker that year. And as a newly divorced, freedom-loving woman, I recall on this heartfelt gathering day, it was sweet to savor newfound independence beyond, but including, that ten-year-old right to vote.

I would not live with mortal eyes to see future freedom-advancing laws, like "no fault" divorce when in California, Ronnie Reagan, movie star turned governor of said state, signed that 1969 small step forward. No need to prove a man's failings for a woman to gain independence from whatever holds her back in life. She can wake up and live, without onerous marriage laws working hard to bind her in place.

In my day, it was not so easily done. "F" for "Failure" might well have been blazoned on my forehead, or so it often felt. Divorce, for starters, carried stigma and raised questions I, then and there, was not prepared to answer. But fellow reporters in my "Thompson crowd," back in Chicago in 1915, had kidded poor "Herb," about an assignment to Biloxi, Mississippi. They "didn't think it was right to send a man who is on the wagon down the Father of Waters with a bunch of Chicago politicians." Perhaps he'd fall off? Should we blame hard-drinking companions?

But I married the man and was perhaps, in part, to blame for son Justin's early life, devoid of a strong father figure. My boy was just nine by the time Herb removed forty miles north, to Croton-on-Hudson. Though that, that was a mere fraction of my failure.

"Oh, nobody knew it except me," I would finally write in *Wake Up and Live!* Truth got told, that "no matter how ingenious and neat the theories were which I presented to myself to account for my lack of success, I knew very well that there was more work that I should be doing, and better work, and work more demonstrably my own."

My response, for myself, and for others? "Act as if it were impossible to fail." There it was, my formula, my message, published in 1936 by the great Simon & Schuster, with Twelve Disciplines to study and put into practice. Millions of copies sold.

On a visit to my penthouse near Gramercy Park, newspaper man Jack Stinett wrote me up as a "shy woman" who "conquered it" with a strictly imposed regimen, turning aspiration to achievement, by way of *Becoming a Writer, Wake Up and Live!* and fiction, too. Mysteries got mentioned ("she reads scores of them, has written one, 'Most Beautiful Lady'). Mysterious nod is given to "another in her typewriter."

My Invincible Aunt is not yet so titled, in my *Wake Up*, best-selling author year.

My passions, Jack told, beyond mountains of mysteries, and "aside from her writing and her 19-year-old son" are "cigarettes (she smokes incessantly)" and "Christopher Columbus, a beautiful four-month-old Maltese kitten." Addictions, might one term my cigarettes and mysteries?

On our travels, we ladies saw a publication in 1963, describing distress like mine, termed by Betty Friedan as "the problem that has no name." That second-wave feminist became loved and reviled, for challenging, by way of *The Feminine Mystique*, a world where men only are in charge, leaving wives at home with the children, high on a purported pedestal. Or divorced and struggling to survive.

Her publisher? W.W. Norton, in 1963 and again, a 50th Anniversary Edition, in 2013.

Then what, for me, after my 1936 rise? After Simon & Schuster put lowly me high on the bestseller list, with Margaret Mitchell and Dale Carnegie, with *Gone With the Wind*, and *How to Win Friends and Influence People*? Yes, I did it. I married a second time around. As the 1920s entered despondent 30s, Seward Collins and I had partnered in his great project, the brilliant *Bookman*, duly converted to the conservative, provocative *American Review*. I managed, edited, put out pithy -- on occasion perhaps cutting -- reviews of popular authors.

As for my own writings, consider, if you will, which of them the publishers of my day saw fit to print. Those about writing, and about living in general. In them, I took a gender-neutral stance, it might be said. Those were my times, a quarter-century before W.W. Norton would brave to print a boldly *Feminine* orientation such as Betty's *Mystique*. Louisa's *Little Women* remained a favorite, in my 1930s heyday. *Gone With the Wind* joined that list, with beautiful women doing battle over which man a girl might marry.

Laura's saga for eager young readers, those wondering about old times in America, launched in 1932 with *Little House in the Big Woods* and would climax in 1943 with *These Happy Golden Years*. Marriage and family remained a fitting end for females, throughout the days of we three fellow travelers of *Mayflower* descent. Sarah's thesis, *The American Woman in Search of Her Independence as Represented in the Novel from 1870 to the 1930's* was far too challenging in 1944, to pass big-time publishing muster.

Sandwiched between *Becoming a Writer* in 1934 and *Wake Up and Live!* in 1936, my own novel about a female and her marriage served to couch gender issues in mystery, where by tradition they so long have lived. *Most Beautiful Lady* is my chronicle of a lovely female sought both for beauty and wealth.

Your dramatic television programs of today repeat many such tales, ending often in similar fashion to my own effort, published by Farrar & Rinehart, in 1935. My character Bill wonders; his companion replies: "That he always meant to kill her?"; "Why, yes, it seems to me now that he must always have had it in his mind, though I wouldn't face it before." Most of us, then and now, turn away from believing in such blatant, brutal, materialistic misogyny, do we not?

For me, no need to wonder. My own wealth paled, in comparison to Sewie's. My looks? They were fair enough, fair to say. Far and above, for Seward Collins and me, intercourse of the mind was our shared, deep, and abiding passion. Our wedding took place in 1936, on Manhattan, the twenty-third of October.

My own explicit writings about male-female matters, few and far between, include an *American Review* critique, after my marriage to Seward. By 1937, I dared use the book review pen to challenge the likes of Steinbeck. *Of Mice and Men* flaunted wax-figure, essentially hateful females, from whom it is an ostensible virtue to flee toward masculine companionship. So I wrote; so I shall repeat. What wallowing in masculine sentimentality, masquerading as toughness, in a sad tale about a huge half-wit and his cowboy protector!

Words likely to offend, and they did. "The Browser" thought I was too mean to Steinbeck in 1937, delivered too many "punches."

That same year after marriage, my *Letters to Philippa* appeared in print, also. When an "Oberlin Professor Selects Finest Novels of 1937," that gentleman, Bongiorno, voiced full agreement with my *Mice and Men* assessment. Of the latter, "written in the vicinity of Hollywood," he states, "a more absurd travesty of reality has seldom been seen anywhere but in that city."

Then "Mr. Bongiorno recommended that before any of the Oberlin students did much reading in 1938 that they obtain a copy of Dorothea Brande Collins' recently published 'Letters to Philippa,' in which the author discusses in letters to a young girl modern fiction." I savor now, as I did then, the professor's credit to me for "a discriminating mind and a sharp tongue," such that "Philips no less than Philippas will find the book a profitable one."

As for "The Browser," having taken offense about Steinbeck, he bided his time. His own review of my 1938 novel (a mystery of sorts, in the works in 1936 as Jack Stinett made note), revealed a profoundly provoked male, poised to do battle and fully set to pan *My Invincible Aunt*. (Before I quote, let me first add "(sic)" to the fellow's misspelling of malice).

"For years the Browser has been looking forward to reading a novel by Dorothea Brande, not with malace (sic), but with curiosity. Because some years ago, he used to read her book reviews in the *American Review* ..." As for *Becoming a Writer* "he thought it a wise book." But when "she ordered us to" *Wake Up and Live!* "The Browser did not like that book," so we read. Granted, the fellow did snidely concede that it "probably did a lot of what we vaguely call 'good'"

Moving on to where said Browser most wants to go, "And now at last he has read a novel by the lady." We shall let his 1938 words speak for the gentleman, as he routinely does, in the third person.

"So far so good, but Dorothea Brande's book finally goes wild when Mrs. Willow becomes the leader of a religion of 'Love,' loses faith in her 'face fix' and disappears into the African desert ... So the lady who 'waked up and lived' becomes an awful mess and Mrs. Brande, who knows so much about teaching others how to write, doesn't do so well herself. ... The Browser is quite sad about it. Honestly.

"He thinks she ought to read William J. Reilly's 'How to Use Your Head to Get What You Want.' It doesn't tell you how to write, but it does tell you how to think. The Browser respects that book for being only what it sets out to be."

For my twenty-first century listeners here at Pulpit Rock, or for you readers, if any, about my travels with Joy and fifteen other real women of the past, may I remind you of, or introduce you to, my Great Aunt Grace?

She disappeared into the Egyptian desert.

The year was 1922.

Back in the day, Grace Thompson (Mrs. Benjamin) Plummer is never again seen alive, by we who still walked the earth. An emergency passport, quickly granted to a son, took him to Europe on a mystery-solving mission.

But my truth, rendered as fiction, lies beyond the grasp of the Browser. That fellow seems to figure I cannot think; perhaps considers this a female problem. So, our real subject, our topic that matters, is the dismissal and demeaning of women in our American history. I did not stoop to complain to, or about, Mr. Browser. More important matters ruled the day. Men, with their Masculine Systems, in an all-male world of governments, had made a mess of things.

At the time of the Browser's complaints about fiction, a second World War was raging in Europe.

Sewie had joined the Isolationists, along with folks like trans-Atlantic flier Charles Lindberg, and diplomat Joseph Kennedy, father of future President John. Accusations of fascist tendencies, of anti-Semitic sentiments, flew around the country and world-wide.

Frankly put, I did not want my son Justin to die, nor did Sewie. Neither did Franklin Delano Roosevelt. Until December 7, 1941. Until Hawaii's naval base, Pearl Harbor, had been set on fire.

My Collins family days, how had they transpired? In late September 1940, Seward's brother leaped from a NYC high rise tower, at the age of thirty-four. One year later, plus a few days more, their mother had withered and died. She was buried next to deceased son, Herbert. Seward and I? We had retreated to Lake Geneva, Wisconsin, for a pleasant rural respite, so we hoped.

But politics were involved, male-dominated; women kept peripheral at best. You will recall, perhaps, that then and now, discussion in polite, social society does not include politics or religion. Any female opinions were of little or no interest to public male figures, for they might even offend. I remind you, also, of the Browser.

But yes, there was reason to be at Lake Geneva. The Yale College-originated America First Committee, sponsored by a Wisconsin-based publication *The Spectrum*, held meetings and did hopeful planning, aiming to avoid the inexorable pull into war. Then December 7 dawned, doomed to live forever in infamy, and isolation was no more.

Old sentiments would haunt us, in the Collins family. The story of gossip columnist Walter Winchell's near-successful campaign against Seward, inducing J. Edgar Hoover to send agents regularly to our Wonalancet home in New Hampshire, is well chronicled by author Michael Jay Tucker. From 1942 to 1944 we were targets, until *And Then They Loved Him*, as Mr. Tucker rightly concludes.

A near-final FBI agent's report, March 1944, cites a main finding: "The subject admitted he had had the misfortune of being an isolationist prior to the U.S. entry into this war. He stated, however that was a thing of the past." July 1944 brought the full conclusion: "no evidence of subversive activity." Case closed.

A long row to hoe, that was, in our agrarian idyll. Just four years later, Alger Hiss at his trial, pitted against reformed communist Whittaker Chambers, was a main topic at our evening dining table. Gilbert listened, absorbed, and gathered knowledge. Even at age nine, he "could tell who the good guys were, and who were the bad."

Hiss might deny his treachery, all life long, but the defective letter "t" on his typewriter provided the smoking gun. His stolen government information, stored by Chambers in a cored-out pumpkin, held the exact same defective "t." Enough evidence, with all the rest, for Seward and me.

How has it all ended, for future generations? Another isolationist holds the highest position of power, a President Donald J. Trump. Is world war looming? No way to tell, but racism and antisemitism, along with white Nationalism, runs rampant in the ranks. Gilbert, I am proud to see, wants nothing to do with this present-day Republican party.

He has a deceased wife, and two daughters, of part Asian extraction. Their gender and heritage deserve respect, and representation. No argument there, about gender equal government.

Yet how, when, as our Joy has oft cried? How might our next four ladies open our eyes?

JOY 13

"I LOVE YOU!"

Three small words, from Thomas Southworth, brought a swift and startling chill.

What meaning lurked within?

Mayflower maidens and young girls who followed were in short supply. Boys and men, in much larger numbers, had flocked to seek New World wonders. Which female conquest would serve best as bounty?

"I want you," my suitor added. He lifted a lock of my golden hair which sent a thrilled sensation hurtling through my veins.

Fear leaped to the fore and cast all hints of pleasure aside.

In an instant, a flashback emerged. I am back in time on this same Duxburrow Trail. Another sort of seeker is barreling bold steps beyond the pale. Taking what's wanted, female flaunted, with the secret safe in a world with men, only men, in charge.

Today at our annual August gathering, with Laura soon to speak, my thoughts return to days long past, when males made all the choices. How long I have yearned for a change! How much I have savored each stage. How grateful we all are, for Laura's sage saving of storied history, halfway through America's fulsome four hundred years.

Writings by a woman for all girls and women, and all boys and men, who care to know our past. Her young pioneer perceptions, with universal feelings, preserved by the power of the pen.

What was it like two hundred years beyond my times, for nineteenth-century girls and for the boys, when teenage years brought thoughts of matings? What were the choices, what was glorious, what was grating? We've heard tell before, and shall now again, with gratitude, lend an ear.

Dorothea's words, a writer's wisdom, came to us bearing glints of brilliant bronze and New York City brownstone. As Laura sets to speak, my eye treasures once more the sage and lime green glimmers of verdant life on the prairie, and in olden-day vast woods.

Straight ahead, no more pause, let *Mayflower* descendant two of three, our Laura, shed her light once more. Her memories serve, always, to inform our common good.

CHAPTER 13

Laura

Laura Elizabeth Wilder (1867–1957) born Ingalls

ON MY MARRIAGE DAY, I declined to obey. In my 1880s world, what great rebellion!

Thirteenth in line to join this journey through time, yet so unlike Dorothea who arrived nine years before me. Unlike Sarah, on board eight years beyond. So much younger than me, each could have been my daughter.

Those two from our *Mayflower* triad, how different their lives from mine! Yet so like my one precious child, my lovely rambling Rose. Whether never married, or duly divorced, all three led lives of a younger generation. Dorothea, Sarah, and my Rose were free to travel the world, when and wherever. Free to lecture, to teach, and to write with grit and abandon. Free to reap fortunes. They pried themselves loose from white male strictures, from those ancient imports of the *Mayflower* days.

Slowly, but surely, it did get better for my fellow *Mayflower* descendants. And for Rose. Three years after Sarah joined our spirit life, applause for female progress filled the airways. "You've come a long way, baby, to get where you got to today." They had their own cigarettes "now, baby," would be the ad men's claimed proof of this patronizing praise.

Dorothea and Sarah, each died in the throes of cancer, well before her time. Fifty-six and fifty-eight years of age, each long before her peers. That, too, must be said.

The perils, perhaps, of girlhood in the roaring Twenties, coming of age in the hungry Thirties, life in the New Deal Forties, or growing despair in the furious Fifties and screaming Sixties.

Yet editor, best seller, poet, professor -- whole new worlds were within the girlish grasp of Dorothea and Sarah. Within the grasp, too, of my own sweet Rose, who would write for the world, until nearly eighty.

For me, eighteen seemed my furthest reach. A career over for teacher Laura, on that same marriage day when I boldly refused to obey. Girls who wed got fired, only single were hired. Barefoot, pregnant, and tied to the kitchen were the prospects for females born on the prairie. Or in the backwoods of Wisconsin.

I speak today, umpteenth time at our beloved Pulpit Rock, about a life we have seen already examined under a microscope by millions. How many of my books, autobiographies, and biographies have been sold? For, yes, my long, long life held a whole new career from age sixty-five onward. The hungry Thirties conquered, now an acclaimed writer, I was famous and adored.

I, a great-granddaughter many times over of Elizabeth, by way of our Joy's favorite charge, Warren son Nathaniel, with ease could pay my way, and bask in newfound praise. To be cherished for truthful tales of old. It was pleasure living out those days.

Yet we see I am suddenly despised in Trumpian times. In 2018 my name was removed from a prestigious children's literature honor, named for me after I received the first award in 1954. Now it is scrubbed of the name Laura Ingalls Wilder. Has backlash to *Mayflower*-style white-male theft of native lands now landed me as a handy villain? My mother lived in dread, then made her fear-filled claim. "The only good Indian is a dead Indian." A true reflection of white ladies' views, in the territories, in our pioneer times.

This rebuke is no real hurt for me, a long-dead historian. Yet pained I am, for the other living women in America who are vilified as we voyagers meet and speak. They are scorned by Trumpian supporters of white patriarchal rule, who seem guided by misogynist and racist instincts. Where did I, polite, good-mannered Laura Ingalls Wilder, get such strong language? My daughter Rose was one to inspire.

How many misogyny targets are there in the twenty-first century? We sadly surmise that hatred of Hillary Clinton, Elizabeth Warren, and Maxine Waters is just the small tip of an angry and giant iceberg. Thus, I have come to support Joy's message of gender-equal representation in a gender-equal government.

Political misogyny will die out over the years, when the American dream of equality is institutionalized; when it is made officially true and real for both genders. That American dream began with a *Mayflower* Compact, endorsed by forty-one white male passengers. Women, with no status beyond wife or daughter, were not deemed fit to sign. We lady descendants choose now to write and speak in our female ancestors' name.

Because one masculine signer, Richard Warren, survived in the shallop that fateful night at Clark's Island, I am here today. His son Nathaniel and Sarah Walker, then their daughter Mercy, birthed a Delano line leading to Pa. Those like me, with Warren ancestry, are said to number in the many millions, perhaps the largest branch of the *Mayflower* tree. Thirty million living descendants in total, if you believe 2019 estimates.

Most will never know their seventeenth century ancestral tale. Many may not care. Truth be told, among our spirit voyagers rests a burden to help bring that history forward in time. Once again, at this rock-side gathering while basking in August warmth, I recall my final moments, when Joy first caught my gaze.

It was a cold winter's day, sixty-two years back. The tenth of February, 1957, to be exact. I was old and weary after ninety earthbound years. I said my somber goodbyes to darling daughter Rose.

The ticking of the parlor clock reached my ears a final time. Behold, a host of female forms from centuries past approached, with Joy and a seagull in her shadow! I saw a hint of crimson from vilified Ann, banished long ago from Massachusetts by angry Governor Winthrop. The glow of umber surrounded Elizabeth, my Warren grandmother many times over, known for her status as the wife of a Compact signer, he a revered male member of the *Mayflower* body politic. Vivid amber seemed to highlight Rebecca, hanged in Salem for no good reason. Cobalt blue emanated from our Mary, famed as grandmother to Benjamin Franklin. Four of twelve who had joined this valiant cause.

Next a purple flash of Phillis, slave girl authoress of poems poignant and profound. Warm mustard yellow, there was Jane, a Franklin, her title "sister" to Ben. Bright glowing quince, signaled dear Abigail, wife to Adams, he who scoffs at her plea to "Remember the Ladies." Delicate fuchsia evoked Sally, slave, secret "concubine" to Thomas Jefferson. Four more of twelve, at the time of my passing.

Golden Lucy, victim to lecherous Reverend H.W. Beecher. Glossy chestnut-brown was a backlight for Louisa, happily unmarried, and conjurer of *Little Women*. Victoria floated in rainbow shine, vilified for her exposure of Beecher and pilloried for her presidential run. In 1872? As a woman? How dare she?! I saw divorced Dorothea, on the 1936 Best Seller List with *Gone With the Wind* author Margaret Mitchell. Two million copies were sold of Dorothea's *Wake Up and Live!* Brilliant bronze and New York brownstone I saw hinted; the reflections of her big city life and backwoods retreats.

Those, the last four of twelve, inviting me into a brave new world. Was I ever glad to see that dozen! Despite my loving family, it had been often lonely and isolated, out there in the big woods, on the prairie. So, too, in my golden years, at my beloved Mansfield, Missouri farm.

Off we went, our sisterhood, together, to revisit ninety years of my life as a female in America. As it was when writing my stories, looking back was easier than the living had been much of the time. Yet we pioneers from the East were stoics. Then, as now, we preferred to savor many a heartwarming moment, and were slow to complain.

There we were, again, with my sister Mary in the back of a covered wagon! A world of wonder awaited on the trail ahead, a little house in wooded Wisconsin fading fast to a murky memory. Ma and Pa sat together on the bench up front, Charles Ingalls encouraging the horses, midst murmured pleasantries with Caroline. We small, blue-eyed children, one blonde, one a brown-haired toddler, gazed in delight as a wild hare flashed across the trail.

I smooth, with tiny fingers, hand-sewn quilts cradling Pa's precious fiddle. It is safe and ready to play, when comfort is needed, out in the western wildlands. Set in our traveling-witness view is a whole era, when family after family moves westward under white curved canvases arched over grey-brown wooden boxes with large spoked wheels. Each steed plods quietly, obediently, too tired to startle at galloping rabbits.

Yet days and nights in Kansas yielded harshly harrowing moments. Hair-raising sights and fearsome sounds, as natives, riled by breach of their treaty with the "white men," prepared for the warpath. On calm evenings, Ma read to Pa from novels like *Norwood*, penned in the year of my birth by the Reverend Henry Ward Beecher.

We girls listened in our bed, transported from our little Kansas cabin to spectacular sceneries back in small-town New England, from whence Pa and Ma's ancestors had ventured. Little did we know that the author, fellow traveler Lucy's nemesis, would bring New York City drama to all the country when standing trial in 1875. But that, that is Lucy and Victoria's story.

We traveler witnesses, in another flash, have made a next stop in the Dakota Territory prairie town called De Smet. There my family had finally settled, once Pa yielded to Ma's wishes. Here I am, a teenage Laura, in the back room at Clancy's dry goods store, stitching sleeves swiftly onto shirt after shirt. Along with fellow female witnesses, I listen again to fury-filled complaints of a mother-daughter pair. Fear-driven talk of "the other" comes to the fore, in face of influx of "the Catholics."

We see a pained look cross my features, disappearing nearly as soon as it arises. My small income was too precious to risk, so I did not complain about such complainers. I needed to remain employed and bring Ma and Pa my earnings; this for me was an 1880s joy. Silently, I endured the mean-spirited talk by those crippled with fear of worship in a fashion different from their own familiar format.

More stops we ladies make, as I, a plucky girl still in her teens, raced the prairie on my pony. Each time, I beat Almanzo on his own strong small steed. We heard Pa saying of Manly, "He's trying to kill her!" My suitor arrived weekly with a buggy and sleek brown Morgan team, wild ones no one else could handle. A full stop was not possible, so I had to nimbly leap in, on those courting days.

I did survive the Morgans, but marriage meant the loss of instructor status. I could no longer teach. The all-male school board was in charge and they made the rules. My small female victory? The pastor and my fiancé agreed to remove the word "obey" from the text on my wedding day.

Our first baby, Rose. Then a new infant boy; his passing was a crushing loss. I escaped with my daughter from a raging fire, leaving our home burnt clear to the ground. For Almanzo and me a near-deadly bout with diphtheria followed. Then a stroke left my Manly struggling back from paralysis. The weather in Florida proved a failure for this Wilder family. A stint with my husband's parents was not our answer. Soon we found a kinder climate for the man of our family, in Mansfield, Missouri. Still, Almanzo did limp for the rest of his days. We ladies bore witness to these many hardships survived and to challenges overcome.

We travelers-through-the-centuries have all compared notes about ways we once garnered courage. The memory of tunes played by Pa on his fiddle, I credit with inspiring "whatever religion I have." From the powerful presence I feel, when recalling bible verses long ago memorized, I am led to surmise: "This is what men call God."

Yet for a woman like me, it is connection to the vastness of nature, to all things great and small, which lasts and grows, lifelong. I remained always inspired by those beautiful sights and sounds from childhood. Pa and Ma took us to gorgeous places, both real and imagined, through travels and through reading.

Then my husband and I, we lifted ourselves by the bootstraps and went to settle where Rose could safely be raised. Missouri, in The Land of the Big Red Apple. Outside Mansfield, Gem City of the Ozarks. A Methodist church there, similar enough to Ma and Pa's Congregational, provided community with other females, and the men in their lives. It provided family-like gatherings in our gentle new climate.

Picnics, barn dances, Fourth of July celebrations. In the local paper, my columns soon illuminate "As a Farm Woman Thinks." I added bits about "the Man of the Place," scattered in on occasion.

We co-travelers through time also witness a puzzling scene in a peaceful setting. Comfortably ensconced in Missouri at our Rocky Ridge Farm, age 76 seemed to suit me. There in the parlor, with my visiting daughter, I enjoyed that afternoon's soothing cup of tea. Yet what loud complaining!

As we lady voyagers witness that 1940s day, I recall what I had been thinking. Bless me, seems I'm back in those *Little Town on the Prairie* days! The Clancy's, they were called in my children's novel. But Clayson was that complaining family's true-to-life name.

Here today, it is my Rose who rails about President Roosevelt and his New Deal public works projects. I listen closely and see myself nodding, as if in agreement. We Wilder women often recalled our own families' years of determined self-reliance.

But do we forget how government deals like the Homestead Act helped us make our way? Do I fail to recall how Mary's School for the Blind was finally funded? What about the helping hand of the grand old U.S. of A.?

Rising from her rocker, Rose heads back to the kitchen, as we ladies witness. I see the tightness in my face soften and remember that long-ago feeling. "Maybe there is some good to be had from these programs?" my mind seems to query. No need to quibble with my daughter, who will return to her Connecticut home soon. I did not like a fuss.

Yet it is true, that men, like those in what is now the state of South Dakota, the ones who told me I could no longer teach, had made all the government choices. They thus determined our lives. FDR was current patriarch of the country, and by the 1940s had been so for over a decade. My divorced daughter, Rose, had long objected to this male dominance. As for worshiping the Lord and being a Christian, "I am not," she has proclaimed.

We are both writers. I was merely local and then graduated to novels for youngsters, about life in the olden days on the prairie. A dozen years for me, 1931 to 1943, of completed books for girls and boys, telling of heartbreak, challenges, and *Little House on the Prairie* joys.

From whence comes my power of description? How did I learn to tell a story well?

My Pa told me, when scarlet fever sent sister Mary's sight fading, "Laura, you must be Mary's eyes." That I would gladly do in the 1800s, and again for Manly in 1915. One of us had to stay, had to see to the farm. That left just one, me, to go see our homesick Rose, and to marvel at San Francisco's great World's Fair exposition. What a glorious celebration of Teddy Roosevelt's achievement in Central

America! All the world was grateful and ready to honor that POTUS's travel-enhancing Panama Canal.

Rose's credits in 1915, by the time of my visit, included byline feature writer for a fancy newspaper. Her address then was Mrs. Gillette Lane, c/o The Bulletin, San Francisco, California. Or better yet, I wrote Manly, send letters to 1019 B Vallejo, San Francisco.

Our daughter's more detailed biography might go back in time, to list Rose's marriage to Mr. Lane in March and then a stillborn baby boy in November of 1909. There would be, too, a fateful surgery dooming future babes. That would mean also no grandchildren for Mr. and Mrs. Almanzo Wilder.

Our girl's books, as a published author, started in 1915, the year of my travels west. There was *The Story of Art Smith,* who, trailing smoke, looped his plane to galvanize Fair crowds. Such sights thrilled me, too, Rose's visiting mother. Those I would describe, for Almanzo, who was holding down the fort, back home at Rocky Ridge Farm.

Many tales told to the world followed, authored by our Rose. There was *Charlie Chaplin's Own Story*, 1916, but that was "withdrawn," ostensibly due to a dispute over embellished prose, accurate in spirit, if not in detail (the same goes for Charlie's later version).

Henry Ford's Own Story, 1917.

In *Diverging Roads,* 1919, Rose's own story was disguised as fiction. By then there was no more Mr. Lane in her daily life. I had written to Manly of our girl's husband in 1915: "money runs through his fingers like water." Rose had more to say, in fiction form: "He was going to cut out the booze." But, well, you can guess what happens.

The Making of Herbert Hoover was published as 1920 dawned.

And the long list includes *Hill-Billy*, mid-decade.

Soon there's *Cindy: A Romance of the Ozarks*, 1928, to name just one more from the twenties.

Let the Hurricane Roar, 1932. Then, same year as my *Little House on the Prairie*, comes her *Old Home Town*. Both in 1935.

Rose told her own versions of Wilder family lives. With *Free Land* in 1938, RWL aimed to open freedom-loving eyes. She recalled her father's family, like mine, "started out in Plymouth Colony, two hundred and fifty years ago this summer." Of that Elder Brewster *Mayflower* branch, our girl claimed, "We just keep going along by main strength and awkwardness."

Rose had forged her own way, with a start as a telegrapher for Western Union in the Kansas City heartland, then landed out West in San Francisco. No university like Dorothea, not in the state of Michigan or the city of Chicago. Nothing like Sarah's fancy Massachusetts Smith College, either, for our girl of double *Mayflower* descent. There was just no way to afford it. Rose was left to rely on her independence, and beautiful, boundless intelligence and strength.

My brave girl presented a poised face to the twentieth-century world, hiding hints of occasional awkward uncertainty. There were no funds for a good dentist, either, in our day, to fix bad teeth and proffer a perfect smile, a perfect first impression. No matter, Rose would rise and thrive.

We see that her 1943 manifesto, *The Discovery of Freedom*, is to this day embraced by Libertarians. With buddy Ayn Rand, and fellow author Isabel Paterson, Rose is claimed by some today to have co-founded a full anti-authority, freedom-loving movement. No coincidence, I shall claim, that this triad is all female.

In the twentieth century, Jim Powell chronicled the group as, "Three Women Who Inspired the Modern Libertarian Movement." As for me, I teasingly called Rose's *Discovery* her American propaganda.

Do I claim credit for my girl's work, or her views? Hardly, although we each grant the other kudos for loving support, always. I had read to a very young Rose, and to Manly, on cozy winter evenings, from works like *Ancient, Medieval, and Modern History*. When "Mama Bess was reading. That was best of all," so my daughter recalls. And our life-long letters lent advice and consent, each to the other.

In the years that followed my 1957 passing, author Rose's income included royalties from my wildly popular books, all benefited by her editing talent and expert eye for drama. Fully warranted rewards, yielded from life-long collaboration, paired with plenteous royalties of her own. So, in the end, Rose endured that high class "problem," when required to pay taxes on bounteous income, until her own 1968 passing. Social Security number 040-38-6564 shows in the records, for newly deceased Rose.

I recall, forty years prior, 1938 back-and-forth communications between my mentoring daughter and me, her mother. Mama Bess asserted adolescent rebellion. "I'm afraid I'm going to insist that the story starts as I started it," I wrote my girl. Let's see if Harper's will take it, done my own way, I aimed to propose. In another book about Laura, the fifth of seven, I was tiring of Ms. Lane's latest editing efforts on *By the Shores of Silver Lake*.

My letter shifted to family matters and ended with a postscript. "Do you ever see Helen? I hear she is in New York." But in the same missive, in defense of my own *Silver* version of my own life story: "We all hated a fuss, as I still do," I remind. Yet conflict still raged, both external and internal. "Change the beginning of the story if you want. Do anything you please with the damn stuff if you will fix it up," I added, in a huff.

Aiming also for discretion, I couched a cry of concern. "It will give you more time for your own work," I penned to Rose.

"You are one of the few writers in the country who would turn down a collaboration with RWL, but go ahead," Rose commenced her written reply.

Her own resistance to my *Silver Lake* version had burgeoned. Rose feared that the manuscript was "too adult." My girl needed my reminder: "Adult stuff must begin to be mixed in, for Laura is growing up."

We both grew, over happy golden mother-daughter years. As many a time I have told, here by Pulpit Rock, she scratched my back, I scratched hers. Her *Free Land* is full of detail harvested from a mother's memory. Rose told Almanzo and Laura's story, in the voice of her father.

I am quick to assure, on minor matters. "Likely you need not feel so badly over the threshing in your story. Threshing could have been done the last of July." After a full account of like farming matters, "So perhaps your story is all right," I concluded. That January 1938 *Free Land* publication began bountiful proceeds for daughter Rose, filling her depleted pockets.

Those earnings, going forward, paid off all debts, leaving plenty to purchase her three Connecticut acres. There, my Rose commenced her own journey, a determined, defiant trip back-to-nature. She lived off the land, free of tyrant-male-FDR authority, with no ration card, no taxable income, and no taxes for years. But a full-fledged "high class problem" was Rose's fate in 1957, when royalties from me kicked in. So, you listeners, time and again, have all heard tell, here by the Rock.

It was male authority that galled the most. A world where women voted, but men remained fully in charge, with a foot firmly planted on the necks of all females. Rose rose in defiance, screaming boldly of all men's, and all women's, pain. This male-female imbalance was, and is, to no one's true gain.

Time now to leap again to my 1957 passing, when Joy came calling, promising a grand new beginning.

The ending of life on earth, for me, had come peacefully. "My tired heart needs to rest," I told my girl. Rose had arrived from her home in Connecticut and spent Christmas, January, and early February, too, on Rocky Ridge farm with me, her weakening mother. "My love will be with you always," I tell my only child. Then take I my leave, three days after I turned the mortal age of ninety.

Did I, Laura Ingalls Wilder, simply rest in peace? My fellow voyagers know otherwise. Here I am in 2019, at the foot of Pulpit Rock with fifteen others (seventeen, when you count Joy and Shadow), all witness to four centuries, to four hundred years of life in America.

But no more fuss from me. Time to hear from Sarah, to savor her views about women and independence, about freedom for both genders! Will you bring us closer to her, dearest Joy?

JOY 14

"WHY ARE BOYS SO SURE they are better than girls?!"

Such endless complaints were met with eternal patience by my loving mother, Luna. They were met also with priceless wisdom, gleaned from centuries beyond our day.

"In future times, with shared knowledge of our sameness, men rise in change of mind."

"Our sameness?" I queried and eagerly prompted Mother, as always, for more.

Amazing nuggets frequently followed, filling my heart with hope for humans, despite dismal days of yore.

"At birth babies are far more alike than meets the eye. Girls and boys have parts more same than different, merely moved to where later needs shall best be met, so that coming together and bringing forth offspring is easy, and couples might best beget."

"Same parts?" I wondered. "Tell just how so!" I commanded, such that my instructress promptly proceeded.

"Girls have a penis, just smaller and by another name. Boys have ovaries, just larger and in another place. Ovaries, testicles. Penis, clitoris." Such matters were dutifully and duly explained by Luna.

Prediction, new conviction, burgeoning balm to salve a wounding bane.

"Better because bigger is no longer a valid claim?"

"Yes, dearest Joy. Less is more, small is big, big is small. What was "better" is no matter. Whether sameness or difference, neither brings shame."

"But in the Bible, Eve, a mere small rib of Adam, is credited with original sin. Is the man not better, for having simply been led astray by female wiles, as touted to this very day?"

Luna's patience never faltered. Her faith in the future was ever stalwart. Belief in me was always offered. "By whom are those tales authored? What think you, Joy, I pray?"

My eyes then opened as I realized: Men's stories were meant only for male glory. Females demeaned hurts everyone, it seems.

"Therein lies truth, dear daughter mine. Should you choose to be our messenger, you have wise news to deliver, somewhere down the line. For their twenty-first century daughters, fathers will sagely start to opine."

And yes, we who gather in 2019, we have seen beginnings, for men and their girls, of a whole new, more honest world. Independence is the goal for both daughters and sons. Mothers join in and insist that the task must get done.

On our travels, we witnessed slow inching of progress forward. Brave women made choices, raised their voices, and wrote even from cloisters. For Sarah, our next speaker, it was from both coasts, America's West and the East. For each nine months guiding as educator at Dominican University, another three here on Clark's Island, where she always found peace.

Soon we shall lend eyes and ears, as once more she stands before us. But first, a pause to ponder, as I did with Mother often, that huge male-female difference. It is girls who clearly, undeniably, get pregnant. It is boys whose role in conception can, and often does, remain deniable, a long-held secret.

We witnessed Sarah's Catholic upbringing and savored her own fling. We saw that, with luck, pregnancy issues were skirted. For others not so blessed, those who suffered from an unwanted condition, there was no termination, no abortion, no safe or legal option. Not until 1971.

Before that landmark Roe v Wade ruling, we ladies bore witness to a numberless line of desperate girls, pregnant out of wedlock, flocking to agencies, often Catholic, to exercise a secret adoption option. What of their adopted-out descendants, biological offspring from those olden days? Forever denied knowledge of their heritage, due to a shaming and blaming culture. By the men who ruled, women (like Eve) were made to shoulder society's castigation. Made to bear children in secret, made to forever deny.

Loree Kerr, descended from my charge Ruth's big sister, Sarah, and from a long line of Soules, might be denied entry to the Mayflower Society in 2019, due to ongoing adoption record secrecy, encouraged by endless shaming of her mother for pregnancy out of wedlock.

"So unfair!" I proclaimed, when my mother foretold the Katherine Ann Soule story of Loree Murphy Kerr. Generations of pain for the Soule family, in a line descended also from passengers Priscilla Mullins, cooper John Alden, and military leader Myles Standish.

That 1950s culture played the blame game, restricting males and females from acknowledging a child born out of wedlock. Adoption was the only legal option and secrecy the only certainty. *I'm OK, You're OK*, was only a faint glimmer in the future.

The truth was discovered a half century later, by the magic of DNA. However, the parents of little Loree were still determined to keep their distance. Shaming continues as the male-dominant battle cry. A beleaguered biological mother feels still that endless need to hide.

Our Sarah is Loree's distant cousin through another ancestry line. Sarah, our fellow traveler, lived close to family stories of this ilk. Cousin Edith's child was never acknowledged by the father. Still, the mother boldly claimed the last name of her son, though she was never married to Reverend Havener. This reminds me of a book I read while traveling. Nathaniel Hawthorne does his best to call the world to task about harshness toward mothers of children born out of wedlock. His work of genius, *The Scarlet Letter*, remains a classic, we see.

As for Loree's mother, I feel compelled to tell her: "Don't be afraid to make a phone call to your daughter. She's an accomplished, intelligent and compassionate woman. You're OK. She's OK. And it's OK to love her!"

And now I turn to Sarah. As always at these August gatherings, I treasure her aquamarine glow. Each time we hear her speak, she has so much to tell, all things we want to know. Please share again your wisdom, dearest Sarah, gleaned from your well-traveled life on the go!

CHAPTER 14

Sarah

Sarah Wingate Taylor (1906–1965) cradle to grave

I OWNED NEAR HALF OF Clark's Island, in mortal life. Then, and ever since, this spot has been my soothing summer home. Until I met Joy in the fall of 1965, dozens of years I came from saintly San Rafael, from my poet professor duties, back to these sainted island shores. And since joining Joy's gaggle, I have again come annually with fearless fellow travelers, fifty-four years more.

In 1620 Ed Winslow survived a near shipwreck, was saved from demise at this rocky island beach, by a male god and a female voice. Luna was there as guide, we ladies do firmly believe. Thus, I stand here now, on this fresh-aired August day, remembering Susanna White who was widowed in the dead of winter, 1621. Winslow's wife, Elizabeth, went to her maker during the first days of spring. Widower Winslow took grieving Susanna as his bride, the first pilgrim nuptials. Ancestors mine.

They married in May, after the *Mayflower*, back to England, had set sail.

There is comfort to be found in patriarchal Pilgrim lore. To survivor Winslow, who fathered Josiah, I owe my title land. From Edward and

Susanna's great-great-granddaughter Lucia, I descend. She to a Watson, owner of this island, long ago was wed. I, her great-granddaughter three times over, on Clark's isle thus made my bed.

We see many a male supremacist mark, brought by ancestral whites from English and Dutch shores. Yet I am grateful to reap my earthly inheritance rewards. Then, like Louisa, with no marriage to bind, I celebrated independence.

Like Dorothea, education paved my path, to write my way in our twentieth century world, all while governments stumbled and fumbled, packed full with white male rulers. For me, a published thesis opened academia's door. My long, long title? *The American Woman in Search of Her Independence as Represented in the Novel from 1870 to the 1930's.*

Yet it would be my deep knowledge of the sainted bard of the river Avon, which took me as a teacher to Dominican College, close by the shores of San Francisco Bay. My specialty? Shakespeare. He, the proud playwright and author of *Taming of the Shrew*.

Each summer gathering, here by my beloved Pulpit Rock, we see, for American women in the millions, how long our search for true independence has been, and shall be. In 1965, I joined our race through time. Our Margaret entered one year down the line. Then? Then we fifteen went to Wellesley commencement, 1969.

Might that young girl-speaker be a disciple of our Dorothea? A beginning to her journey, her graduation words inspired an all-female class to rise in a seven-minute standing ovation. What end result, what sort of creation, is Miss Hillary Rodham making? "The challenge that faces us now," we heard her tell, "is to practice politics as the art of making possible what appears to be impossible."

I? I was born nearly a half-century prior to Miss Rodham, in an era when women did not vote, when even a trip to the polls, for fellow females, was truly impossible.

Yet those who had scoffed at suffrage were left to eat their words, as I reached the tender age of fourteen. Unlike my *Mayflower* ancestors, it was not their male God to whom I gave praise on enfranchisement day. I was confirmed a Catholic as a child, but as an adult I well knew that Alice Paul, along with generations of her female fellows, could claim the credit for suffrage survival and their 1920 success.

Now, in 2019, I wonder who will champion our gender-equal government message? Who will wear a crown of thorns? Who will be present to bear witness, when success is garnered, grasped by the horns? Can we give the lie to those today who scoff and claim, "Not in my lifetime!"?

Will women fill half of Congress' seats, pull equal weight, and ensure protection? Will Margaret's *Family Limitation* become accepted as routine, a woman's right? So many issues, so many questions!

Times have changed since the 1920 victory, even since the 1930s that followed. A girl like my cousin Edith, would have a much easier time in the twenty-teens. Conception of a child, before or without marriage? As we ladies stand at my ancestor's first place of worship, those are two of many options we see in these twenty-first century days.

Back in my day, it was not at all the same. Girls like Cousin Edith wore a secret shame, all while Reverend Havener prepared weekly to preach of God and his glory. Fourteen more years I had gained, since the winning of that long-fought right to vote. By 1934, when I was twenty-eight years old, Edith gave her newborn Wingate, and herself also, his father's Havener name. Not a wife to be, so it seems, but a working girl, a dressmaker, she would remain. Havener married another, raised a family with her, not Edith.

What have we travelers since seen evolve for girls in the government realm? Would we see a female step into the room at the highest level by the year 2016? A woman ruler, standing proudly in the Oval Office? Would her name be Hillary Rodham Clinton, speaker at the 1969 Wellesley College graduation celebration?

No. No is our fateful answer. In the name of racism and misogyny, we voyagers witnessed that female goal doomed to failure. Trump and Putin, they hated her. They would not have it.

"Witch!" finger-pointers proclaimed, when Democrats offered for nomination renowned Hillary Clinton's name. "Witch hunt," Republicans cried, as Mueller uncovered Trump and Putin's multi-leveled criminal enterprise.

So, clearly, life's path for a girl like me, born in 1906, would have traditional restrictions. I had no government visions; there was no room in a democracy for me. Wife, nurse, or teacher, in the service of raising the children who are America's future, those were my possible considerations.

Or, perhaps, the stage?

I could easily pursue my love of Shakespeare during my Smith College years. Like Hillary at Wellesley, but for me many decades earlier, I was surrounded only by women. Amidst those all-female days, my performances brought measured praise. But I came face-to-face with the truth: I lacked the sang-froid and tiny me sorely lacked the stature of a Sarah Bernhardt.

Higher education, perhaps the halls of academia, might be most suited as my place. Meanwhile, around Europe I chased, studying, traveling, and viewing the Masters in arts and literature of the day. My return to the States, and my Catholic upbringing, landed me with the Church's Boston newspaper. At *The Pilot* my own poems were put to print, among a long list of others, vetted by me as Poetry Editor.

Boston College, another Catholic sponsor, supported my *Independence* thesis efforts. This rendered me a ticket to the West, where Catholic girls could be my pupils, at that hallowed Dominican College.

The campus chapel in winter. Clark's Island a sanctuary in the summer. With a boat trip on Sunday, I rowed myself to a Duxbury church Mass. Back on the island I puttered in my unmechanized

Cedarfield haven, and sometimes taught class. Does it seem a lonely life? Never to be married, never to be a wife?

Oh, I had my fling. With my sister-in-law's little brother, if truth be told. And Cid, my fellow lover of Duxbury and her lore, told a story true to the spirit of my kind.

"There is a village south of Boston, not far enough down to be called the Cape," she started that 1953 novel, *The Hornbeam Tree*. "This village on the south shore had its quota of lone women," so the story of Miss Eva was told. "Not a widow, she had never married. She was the one who stayed and took care of Mama and Papa and finally Brother Henry."

After all her family were dead and gone? Eva had her fling, full of heartfelt longing and consummate passion. Truly a joy, truly satisfying. After all of that, for Eva, or for me?

Oh, I had my teaching, and my writing, my books of poems, of verse. First *Samphire, Herb of St. Peter*. Then Pilgrim-inspired passions, *Yankee Island Ballads*, and *Clark's in Plymouth Harbor*.

Holding on to my heritage, planning for Clark's future, was passion enough for the following days of my life. Friends and students came to join me here, on this sainted island. Long traditions continued. Our Louisa had visited in the century prior, as had her cherished friend Mr. Thoreau, those two of *Little Women* and *Walden Pond* fame.

Truman Capote worked on his *Breakfast at Tiffany's* through a summer by these wave-lapped shores. Holly Golightly, his composite creation, an unattached, unconventional wanderer, emerged here from darkness to light. Now, added twentieth-century creative writers I aimed to gather in 1965.

All interrupted by my own untimely demise, that year post-summer's end.

Interrupted, also, by Joy's arrival.

Since then, on our travels, informed by heritage and blessed independence, I have witnessed, grown weary, then arisen to fight again the good fight. With fellow ladies, I conspire. Let us make

America a better place, with freedom for both of our genders. Let us move forward, and onward, on to the land of GEG.

I have told many an anecdote at our annual gatherings, here at Pulpit Rock. Proud to be followed, always, by our Margaret, adored female champion. Again today, I take my leave, in the interest of all that follows.

Once more, I yield to Joy.

JOY 15

"WHY DOES A NATIVE LEADER, who you say will be known as King Philip, lose his head?"

Decapitation was a far too familiar reality in Plymouth, where Wituwamat's head sat on a spike for a year or more. By the 1630s, those storied times were long past. Yet Luna foretold a similar fate for Massasoit's son, half-a-century down the road.

"Will Philip's head really be posted on display, for all to see, for decades beyond his defeat?" I wondered aloud.

"If you choose to bear witness to centuries to come, such truths sadly will be revealed," I heard replied.

"We came as immigrants, welcomed by many natives, reviled, in the end, by others," Mother always said. "For centuries in this land, more will come, from near and far. Each recent wave embraced or met with a wall of resentment."

"Each brings their preferred religious beliefs, with a common theme, the perpetuation of patriarchal control. Jews, Muslims, Catholics, Protestants of varied ilk, each yearns for a male protector, supreme above all others."

"Should you accept your mission, my Joy," Luna warned, "you shall find this planet nearly subsumed, three centuries hence, by conflagration based on conflicting religious belief."

The first time I heard Mother speak of this matter, a shiver slid up my spine.

"Not once, but twice, many tens of millions will die or be wounded. 'The War to End All Wars' the first will be called. 'World War II', the second becomes."

"So, the first becomes World War I?" I asked with sickening sensation.

"Yes, my child, sad but true," Luna answered my query, then told of that monstrous second conflict.

"Jews will become a reviled enemy, to a German leader with the name of Adolph Hitler. Beheading will be replaced by mass exterminations in concentration camps where victims are gathered by the millions."

I forced myself to ask, in dread, a one-word question, to which I received a one-word answer.

"How?"

"Ovens."

"Will there be a World War Three?" I pleaded next to know, yet Luna had work to do, that day, as did I.

Master Alden had returned from far to the north, at the Kennebec River outpost, trapping furs to offer in payment for their longstanding debt to the Adventurers, as Plymouth Colony financiers were titled. Our evening meal would celebrate a happy family reunion.

Soon enough, I found a moment to pester my mother once more about religious difference and war.

"Times will change, in more ways than one," Luna promised while gazing into my anxious, earnest blue eyes.

"More, please. More!" I begged and was mercifully met with word of men with new ideas, men like a man named Sigmund Freud.

"He will come to be known for great advances in thought, and for a far-reaching goal, to go beyond religion with reason and science."

"Will that help?" I hopefully asked Mother, then held my breath for her reply.

"Not much, in his own lifetime. Freud is a Jew, who flees Hitler's Nazis in Austria in 1938, and dies in England in 1939, as war begins with the dictator's invasion of Poland."

"But the seeds are sown, with progress certain to follow," Luna reassured.

And today in 2019, we see like efforts continue, offering great promise. We fellow voyagers have watched the son of POTUS 40, Ronald Reagan Junior, on the same big screen where ads for Franklin Templeton Investments flash images of Jenny's brother, Ben. "This looks promising!" I heard several of my fellow females agree.

There is a Freedom From Religion Foundation, we are told. "I'm Ron Reagan," we hear the former President's son announce, "an unabashed atheist, and I'm alarmed by the intrusions of religion into our secular government." As we gather at Pulpit Rock in 2019, we ladies could not agree more.

Yet something called the Religious Right and conservative preachers of varied kinds, rant against perceived rejections of their God and his "sinless" son, Jesus. One writes in 2018 of our Margaret, gone from the earth fifty years and more.

Preacher David Schrock laments that, to his mind, our fellow traveler's "illicit views of sexuality have led generations of women away from God." A white male minister is decrying perceived betrayals of his patriarchal, white male God, a deity considered supreme by those who call themselves Christians. Schrock recommends a book he reviewed, by Presbyterian Pastor George Grant, with a title that speaks volumes to the challenges women still face. *Killer Angel: A Biography of Planned Parenthood's Margaret Sanger.*

My mother had warned me of these challenges to come.

"Viewing independent women as evil will be the modus operandi of many champions of Christ in the twenty-first century. Future traveler Margaret is a case in point. Yet others will step to the fore, a president's son included, to bring freedom from such religious tyranny."

I breathed a sigh of relief when Luna spoke those words.

"Is it true? A Ron Reagan will do battle with a Religious Right in the twenty-teens, so that life will improve for both women and men?" I begged to hear this confirmed.

"Yes, my dear child. It shall be so," fell as music to my ears, just as Mistress Alden appeared at Luna's side, to pronounce our next tasks. No more pestering of my mother, for me, on that day.

The next chance I had to query, comfort was followed by terror when Luna told of Trump. I shuddered to hear about the theft of the 2016 election from a first mainstream female candidate for President of the United States. Aided and inspired by strongman Putin, a fury-filled Commander in Chief would form a forty-fifth executive administration steeped in protectors of patriarchy. Women's choice to access all available birth control options, so courageously pioneered by our Margaret, would be on the blocks, I heard tell.

Kavanaugh, as a new Supreme Court Justice, would be one of countless steps aimed to keep females firmly entrenched under the weight of male dominance. Luna told also of women's resistance, each step of the way. Mother's days were numbered, she advised in the face of my pleas for more stories. Would there be success for advocates of feminine rights to ownership of one's own body? Such queries from me gained from Luna a frequent reply. "Should you choose a mission to witness four hundred years, my child, you shall see with your very own eyes."

Our forty-ninth gathering has followed events of 2019 which continue to chill beyond measure. February brought an early attack on Title X family planning protections for low-income women across America, first offered half-a-century back. Affordable birth control with the full range of contraceptive methods, as made possible since 1970 by that federally funded program, should now take a back seat to abstinence-only education and risk-taking avoidance of coupling when likely fertile. No wonder this kind of legislation has been termed a War on Women!

Trump appointees prefer women forgo the Pill, IUD, or other pregnancy protections, to instead follow a prescription in line with the Catholic age-old edict. The National Women's Health Network, based in DC, will rise to that challenge, we have been assured by Director Cindy Pearson.

In 1971, here by our granite monument, we first heard from our own Margaret's lips her tales of a forceful fight for female freedom. We heard of her calls for each woman to choose the fate of her own body. This she has told, and re-told, ever so well. Each time, sparkling in my vision I see shiny blue ribbon.

In this August moment, here at our latest Pulpit Rock gathering, I shall pause my own account of past and present. It is the mother of birth control from whom we all must now hear. Please speak once again, fellow traveler, of trials and triumphs, and of better things to come.

CHAPTER 15

Margaret

Margaret Sanger (1879–1966) born Higgins

I, SIXTH CHILD OF ELEVEN, could not save my mother. So, I aimed to save the world. In my day, masculine fury raged, standing steadfast in my way.

First, in 1904, I saved my sister's baby from a frozen snowbank, where the drunken father had tossed her.

Then I did battle with Catholic religious restrictions demanding that women bear unwanted offspring, bowing down to men's desires. My answer? *Family Limitation* in 1914. Then, in 1916, *What Every Girl Should Know*.

The reply from men in charge? Arrest, over trumped up claims of "obscene" literature sent through government mail. Years of public spectacle, days and months in jail.

My sister's child, Olive, was in her grandmother's care, while my sister, on a hunger strike, trumpeted female despair. In the face of male obstruction, Ethel shared my passion to make this world more fair.

Who would truly save us from these twentieth-century masculine oppressions?

Wonder Woman, the new comic heroine -- would she be the answer? My niece Olive, rescued from a snowbank to become my fellow prototype for that legend, would dodge many a male bullet during a long, secret life. Women today, in 2019, must still do battle with patriarchal powers pulling rank in government, attempting again to remove a female's greatest protection. Birth Control.

Yes, I am the mother of Planned Parenthood. Revered and reviled, to this very day in 2019. My earthly journey complete, I was met in 1966 by Joy, Shadow, and all female friends here gathered. Save Cid, last but not least, who joined four years beyond my afterlife arrival. What wonders we have witnessed, traveling together through this last half-century forward.

Those clinics sister Ethel and I opened, how they blossomed, oh so slowly over time. Brave defenders championed the fight to save female lives. Now, so many have died.

Religious Right reactions repeat their furious fire. Bullets shatter plate glass. Doctors, in pools of blood, expire. The law be damned is the rant. Forget Roe v Wade is the chant. Abortion's a sin. Their "righteous" crusade is to kill those who choose it. Deadly, desperate measures to protect those Masculine Systems.

My biography, my life, begun one-hundred-forty years back? It has been written many times and is easily found, for those who care to witness how others expound. My *Autobiography*, my own voice exposing, is still yours for the asking, for those who care to open eyes and ears. My niece Olive, and the *Wonder Woman* saga? Again, Jill Lepore does justice to one of our number, this time in *The Secret History*. Another fascinating read, like Jane's *Book of Ages*.

Yearly, by this Pulpit, we females speak, each for herself. What bears repeating, for me, this final round? I have a plea, for future generations, to remember with me the moment my own father, Michael, at long last, waxed profound.

The battle year was 1914, as you've heard this story told. The booklet *Family Limitation* was boldly sent to the judge, as I fled to

Montreal and then London, to postpone my trial, gathering worldwide support and publicity for our cause. All to the horror of my longtime widower father.

Hysteria? Nervous breakdown? He voiced paternal concerns and speculated on his daughter's state of mind, in light of blaring newspaper headlines. Then he made an overdue choice, to become informed, to skip journalistic translations, and go straight to the source. At long last, Mr. Michael Hennessey Higgins began to read and to see for himself what his daughters are thinking, saying, and writing in each issue of *Woman Rebel*.

The result? Somberly and sadly, he wisely stated: "Your mother would be alive today, if we had just known all this then."

Those words, I shall plead once more, need be remembered. Let women choose for themselves. That is what this means. What blocks such obvious wisdom? Male white supremacist dreams, inspired by age-old Masculine Systems.

That, that patent travesty, is why I join my fellow travelers, as our knowledge of selves and others evolves, in a much-needed mission of mercy, bringing joy and peace to our twenty-first century world.

Make government equal in power, fifty-fifty, both genders. Put the wisdom of Michael Higgins, together on equal footing, joined with the wisdom of his daughters. With gender equal government, the world can be saved. Wake up, America. Enter the land of GEG!

JOY 16

LUNA AND I NEVER SPOKE of what happened to me, there on the Duxburrow Trail. Yet she knew. And she knew that I knew that she knew. Many tales she chose to tell. Those tales told me that she knew.

"Four centuries hence, minus a decade or two, a chorus of voices will be heard. A whole movement will be born." As I speak here today, repeating Mother's words from long ago, it is like my first time, when I shivered in delight, as she consoled with music to my ears. Her gentle gray eyes seemed to gaze through my own anxious blues.

"Tell me more," I beg, as I hardly dare breathe.

"A 'MeToo' choir shall harmonize in empathy for all girls and women, and the boys and men in their lives. Story after story of thoughtless, selfish, heartless, often cruel deeds, will finally be told. Perpetrators of abuse will sit in a spotlight, viewed around the world by all. A day in court will be had, over and over, by victims of those who used their size, and the power of a 'males only' world, to lord over women and girls."

"Like poor Lidia Fish, in that 1677 story you have foretold?" I shiver again, this time in dread, as I recall Luna's account of a young girl's plight. A relative, Ambrose Fish, will be whipped, not hung, though capital punishment for rape had been entered into Plymouth Colony law in 1636.

"Yes, my dear child, like that in a way. Abusers must be held to account. But in the 2020s, death will no longer be a possible penalty for such a crime. A more measured justice will be had."

"Because of gender-equal government? Is that why courts become more just?" I am recalling Mother's oft-repeated promise to my recurring query, "Will there truly be gender-equal government, in those centuries to come?"

"Ah, yes, my dear girl," Luna on occasion replied.

"But, when?" I endlessly would plead.

"When people start talking, describing, openly, loudly. After nay-sayers have been heard, as all call for solution."

"Then how, what, where, when?" I cried out, in angry despair.

"When women come together, powered with spoken and written word. Some right here in Duxburrow, on the island where you were born." With such words, Mother, again, would start to soothe. Reassured for brief moments, I returned to my chores, gathering shellfish from mudflats of Bluefish River inlets, drenched in golden sunlight with little Ruth at my side.

As we worked and played, I also pondered. "Why cannot females come together now, to speak our truth and claim our rights? Surely a chorus of voices could be gathered in less than four centuries time!"

Soon enough, her child's desperate need to know yields patient offers of more, from Luna.

"The truth emerges that without fifty percent representation by women for women, without fifty percent representation by men for men, a system is unfair, unkind, often cruel. In such a system, in its lack of fifty-fifty definition, misogyny is left free to rule."

"Then what happens? Who will care? What will they do?"

"Male founders, in our new country, will at first chose an unfair Constitution. Females then gather males around them, willing and able to build strength in that growing America. Together they add fairness to the structure, creating something new."

"Really? Truly?"

"Yes, together, men and women, will birth a fifty-fifty rule." Luna's balm to my ears further blossoms.

"Mysteries of science must unfold, weaving a vast foundation of knowledge to encourage and to support both genders, in the journey to become stronger together,"

"Like the knowledge you say will lead to the nuclear code?"

"Yes, and like Watson and Crick. Like the double helix, the mysteries of DNA. Like twenty-three chromosomes, working their magic. Like a human genome project, telling the world we are all related, helping us understand how. Like a worldwide web, with electronic communication, making shared knowledge available to all beings who read, write, and use their digits to tap a keyboard. With websites that are free, like Wikipedia and WikiTree, and websites for which people pay. With Ancestry.com among them, a worldwide coming together shall slowly but surely emerge. With Twitter, and Instagram, and Facebook, and more."

"And more?" I urged my maternal mentor. "How will I, if this mission accepted, make your, my, our fellow ladies' voices heard, and our message remembered?"

"A system will have grown, with long, honored traditions. Publishers are known for fine reputations. Phillis, our first aided by them, her words put to print, for eager readers waiting."

When pestered, Luna continued, with delicious details.

"Louisa will find a Roberts Brothers, then W.W. Norton. Victoria, bold rebel, will have to self-publish. Then Dorothea, her start is with Harcourt, Brace, but climbs next with her *Wake Up!* to famed Simon & Schuster. Laura will be helped often by HarperCollins. It seems no mainstream publisher for the mother of birth control. But Mrs. Sanger's *Happiness in Marriage* may make it to print at Blue Ribbon Books, something tells me."

Colors flashed before my eyes, as Luna spoke of future supporters of women writers in America, from Phillis to Margaret Sanger. "Royal purple meets my eye," I exclaimed, "when you say Phillis! Chestnut brown at your mention of Louisa. And a beautiful rainbow for Victoria. Brilliant bronze and brownstone, it seems, for Dorothea. For Laura, sage and lime greens appear in my vision. Now Margaret conjures a royal blue ribbon. My senses cry out, dear Mother, that those ladies want to meet me."

Luna, I could see, was not surprised by my description, nor by my strong feelings and next question. "There is one more hue, a lovely gray and white mix with hint of dusty rose, like a glorious sunset that rises in my view as I wonder also, what about Cid?"

Promptly Luna replied, "For Cid, it shall vary, but mostly Bobbs-Merrill."

"Who will I find, if I make a future venture?" is my final query. But for my heart, relief still escapes.

"Time will tell, my dear child, now our bedtime awaits."

All this, I came to believe, I must see with my own eyes. Meanwhile, I lulled my own charge, Ruth, off to sleep with her sisters. My daily tasks completed, I settled down to rest heart and weary limbs.

And to plumb a misty land of GEG, forming faintly in my dreams.

CHAPTER 16

Cid

Cid Sumner (1890–1970) born Ricketts

TWENTY-TWENTY. AN UPCOMING ANNIVERSARY, for lovers of America and her history. Celebrations are planned, here and abroad, to mark an arrival made monumental to a nation. This country will be a mere two-hundred-forty-four years of age. Millions will look back, a full four hundred years, to when our sainted ship, the *Mayflower*, in November of 1620, reached Atlantic shores. Seeds of democracy were then sown, along with the seeds of fellow travelers, Sarah, Laura, and our Dorothea, with multimillions more to follow.

Perhaps readers of our tales, when published, will come from among the rolls of those thirty million estimated living Pilgrim descendants. And from the multimillion descendants of migrants who followed, like we thirteen fellow female voyagers. From the multimillions more, as well, descended from natives of these invaded lands. Or from those descended from slaves, owned long ago by tens of thousands of citizens, and by twelve American Presidents. Joined, perchance, by endless numbers of eager, voluntary immigrants to follow, in distant times, or more recent. Like Donald Trump's mother, arriving 1930. To each, we give a share of credit for America's character, for her flaws, and for her greatness.

Joined also, we dare hope, by readers of all ages, from elder statesmen like former President Bill Clinton to young, single women in Congress, like Alexandria Ocasio-Cortez, not yet in her thirties. Perhaps by 2020 Presidential candidates, Democrats and Republicans, female and male. By Senators Corey Booker, Kamala Harris, Kirstin Gillibrand, Lindsay Graham, Bernie Sanders. Perhaps by another ex-Massachusetts Governor, William Weld, and by representatives for the good of America, of every color and stripe.

A fight, we see, in the making, for all American lives. A fight, so that Democracy can survive. Will a twenty-first century Elizabeth Warren, who shares a married name with our fellow traveler, find time to read these pages, while her fight for the U.S. Constitution rightly rages?

Twenty-twenty. Also, posthumous jubilee for me, I see. My fifty-year October day of remembrance, it seems, not to be forgotten. Private celebrations at the least, I hear, are planned by my descendants.

Yes, having reached the age of eighty in 1970, my ordinary extraordinary life ended here in Duxbury with a fateful twist. And there to greet me, both Joy and Shadow, with their host of historic women.

We are grateful, Luna, that you saved the day in 1620, here by Clark's Island shores. Without you, we could not all be gathered together for this final magic moment in August!

On the occasion of our 2019 consummate reunion, I take my ultimate turn, with a touch more of my story, so oft repeated. Shall we go, again, to where my one small life began?

To a Southern town, in the heart of Mississippi. Way down yonder.

Let us pause for that 1893 moment, as Mother and two doting aunts muse over their precious toddler's placid nature. "Cid" becomes my only name, "Bertha" cast aside. One aunt tends the chickens, the other minds the cows. I am the adored child, cherished also by three big brothers. I am alone, by myself, in this recovered memory. I feel a great vastness around me, where added comfort is to be found.

You ladies have heard all about the in between, my long list of challenges and achievements, travels and adventures. No biography to date, but my granddaughters foretell of just such a project. Perhaps the result will highlight a moment in my sixty-seventh year, as I mull in my writing about *Faiths for a Complex World*, published in "The American Scholar." I think of my piece as *Way Down Yonder*.

As last to speak today, I asked Joy, who gladly acquiesced, if I might simply quote, a bit, the voice, my voice, of a female turned 67 in 1957. "First, let me go way down yonder by myself. What do I find in such a quiet, lonely place? I find myself, my real self, one not molded and held in shape by the circumstances and complications of my life. I feel, I know, that there is Something greater than I, a delectable force, a power, a source of joy and light from which I receive sustenance not only sober but gay, and courage for the body's pain and the heart's grief. Do I call it 'God'? No, I do not choose man's 'distortion.' I can only call it Something.

"To me, good and evil are like a see-saw evenly balanced with man standing in the middle and able to throw his weight now this way, now that, and so tip the scales. I can only hope that good will thus in time overbalance evil as man learns better."

Today, in 2019, I have come to trust that men and women will be joining together, fifty-fifty, to form a new world of government that is truly gender equal. That there will, sooner rather than later, be a land of GEG.

My *Way Down Yonder* words, by the way, were printed in the same publication year as *Traveler in the Wilderness*, which chronicled one of my many journeys. I was the only woman in a party of eight explorers, on expedition through the vast canyons of the Colorado River as she flowed, whether ferociously or in peace, toward the great Gulf of Mexico. That was the same year as *A View from the Hill*, with six decades of reminiscence. I shall offer a sample from that view.

Join me for another journey, if you will, on two late September days back in 1943, when my daughter Deedee's first child was due. Travel from Boston to Texas brings a pair of peak moments. For me, a fourth grandchild is in the offing. For soldiers on the train I ride, packed close as sardines, lovers left behind are on their minds, with hopes and dreams of a return to their lives, perhaps, with career, marriage and children.

"I set my small collapsible bag down and myself upon it, knees drawn up to my chin, all in a squinch. There with my back against two hard iron rods, I sat all night, yet I remember it as one of the most interesting of my life, and one of the most rewarding.

"I felt so apologetic for taking up even this small an amount of room that I felt I must do something to make amends. Once I had had some skill at reading palms, so now, peering up at the tall sergeant who loomed over me, I tugged at his boot strings till he looked down. 'Would you like me to tell your fortune?'

"That was the beginning. All night I read palms. Sometimes I could see nothing but the hand thrust between the legs of those standing around me, and an ear presented at the side of someone's khaki knees. By morning, since I had to speak above the rattle of wheels directly under me, I was so hoarse I could barely make myself heard.

"At dawn some of the soldiers who were packed on the inside of the coach got out, and then I had a seat for the rest of the day. And what a day! Those boys plied me with apples, coffee, chewing gum, cokes and doughnuts. They sat beside me, saying, 'You know it was funny, your saying that to me -- 'And then I would hear about home and their girls and what they wanted to do in the world if they ever got home again. So this night and day journey became a treasured experience instead of a nightmare."

And I must repeat also, in honor of fellow voyagers like Phillis and Sally, a bit more about writing on girls of color, back in 1946 and 1949. First, the novel *Quality*. From Nathaniel Rothman, in The Saturday Review, a synopsis suffices. "Mrs. Sumner's story is about Pinkey Johnson, a beautiful young octoroon who can pass in white society and has already done so at college. Now she has returned to her family in a Mississippi town, to face the terrible consciousness of her place in that society."

From famed American linguist and educator, future Senator Seth I. Hayakawa from California, born Canadian child of Japanese immigrants, came a welcome 1946 tribute in Book Week. "Mrs. Sumner, white, and born in the South, has written a book of genuine human insight and social perception. I hope it becomes a best seller." Yes, both loved and reviled, my effort survived to become a much-watched movie, *Pinky*.

Second, I recall my 1949 offering titled *But the Morning Will Come*. My heroine learns her baby will have "negro" blood, which her secretive, self-despising husband has always sought to hide. Will she end her pregnancy, or give the child away? Not for a moment does she consider the matter of color a reason for such a choice. In the end, another man becomes her champion, raising with her a cherished baby boy.

The Mississippi plantation where my mother was raised had not all that long before been home to hundreds of slaves. From my Aunt Edwina we have a white female's memoir of "back in the day." But *What About Angry White Men?* is not a title I myself would brave.

Yet my friend Eudora Welty would rise to the 1960s challenge, channeling the mind of a white man in 1963 as he murdered black civil rights leader Medgar Evers. In *The New Yorker*, Eudora moved our country inches forward through the mud of our quintessential, horrifying American controversy. We peeked into a racist male mind, by way of her brilliant short story *Where is the Voice Coming From?* Women of the South, raising our voices.

Controversy, in the forties or the sixties, was no real surprise. What strikes me today, I stand here to say, is the persistence of mean-spirited reactions based on mere skin color variations. A President draws followers daily, as we speak, based on the worship of whiteness. Acceptance of color, remains by some termed "propaganda!" From the website Mississippi History, a 2018 excerpt from my biography shall serve as my exhibit.

"Sumner published her first novel, Ann Singleton, in 1938 but did not capture the public's attention until her second novel, Quality (1946), a *propagandist* work opposing segregation." To "propagandist," if my words be written, I suggest italics be added.

Again, you here today have heard this before. And of daughter Bobbie's life with husband John Cutler, running a "Mom & Pop" business, publishing a small-town paper. That still ubiquitous *Duxbury Clipper*. After grandson Robert, four more Cutlers to follow, in the forties and fifties. By 1961, you have heard also of John's book, *What About Women?*

We travelers know that women, like all of color, have been much segregated out of the white male world, from *Mayflower* days forward. Thus, in my 1961 Foreword written for John Cutler, my thought was, and remains, "Here it is, a book that holds between its two covers a vast quantity of fascinating information, truly startling in its implications. It gives us a new perspective on what has been happening, gives us a look at possible future developments, and may even help us decide what we are going to do about it all." In 2020, if I may rephrase, we shall determine what happens next.

In the old days, my most popular stories, by far, were of a white girl who, determined to gain an education, then reaches her goal of love and marriage with her college professor. From 1948, to 1961, to 1965, *Tammy Out of Time*, *Tammy Tell Me True*, and *Tammy in Rome*, tell the story of our times. White men in charge. Today, in endless ways, females still await a change. Toward that end, we sixteen travelers have gathered.

It is time for truth of another kind. Truth revealed, in part, by the tale of my passing. That tale I am now set to recall, for benefit of men and women alike, and for freedom from male dominance and misogyny, thus for freedom, truly, for all.

That day in October? The year 1970? When Joy, Shadow, Anne, Elizabeth, Rebecca, Mary, Phyllis, Jane, Abigail, Sally, Lucy, Louisa, Victoria, Dorothea, Laura, Sarah, and Margaret came to call? There was little Ricky, my darling grandson, Bobbie's fifth and last child. A fellow night owl, late on a Saturday eve, standing at my door.

Just that morning, his brothers had come to mind. Tidying up, my hand smoothing the bedcover one final time, "making it right" at the start of my day, I thought of firstborn grandchild, Robert. A next brother, David, also. They'd had a military training, teaching perfect execution for Army, or Marine, morning boot camp inspection.

My youngest grandson loved me dearly. I loved him dearly back. Too dearly for a "yes" from the adored "witch" of a grandmother, on that fateful eve. No dollars for drugs, that Saturday night. Next we knew, there I was, ascending through death's door. Welcomed by Joy, and my fellow travelers through time. AP, and that magazine, *Time*, helped spread word round the world. "Murdered by her grandson."

"Everyone loved her," 1970 tributes trumpeted. A most glowing paean by son-in-law John. Yet "Here comes the old gray witch," is what he had sputtered to his children, when my car could be seen, arriving in their Duxbury driveway.

For that I shall hold him to account, as he likely knew I would. Truth must be told. I aim to shed light, foster healing, over time, in my own way. Women and girls, men and boys, across America and all around the world, long lists of them need to be heard. For all of them, we traveling spirits shall work our magic, if only from beyond the grave.

Because, as we ladies have all seen, just as vilification of non-whites goes on in America today, vilification of females goes on, and on, and on. Rebecca was labeled witch, I was labeled witch, Hillary is labeled witch, with many more to come, unless finally put to a stop.

So here I am, today, with my fellow ladies, with Joy, and with Shadow.

We are the joyful dead. Not because of that heaven conceived by men so long ago. If words can describe, it is because of that place way down yonder. There we went to ponder, while mortal. There each of us wandered, alone, afraid, or undaunted, to pass into the great beyond. There we became fully part of all that ever was, is, and will be.

Now, in 2019, we who have joined in this 2020 mission, we gather together once more. Not to ask the Lord's blessing. We are here to make our voices heard. God, whoever or whatever she or he may be, helps those who help themselves. That we shall do.

At each passing, Joy joined us. "It gets better," she promised. "Come with," she proffered. Then guidance, she offered. "What key opens doors, to get sanity back? It is simple, in truth. It's not about sinning. Time to go back, to honest beginnings."

Now truth has been told, again and again, by women, about themselves; by women, about men.

Anne trumpeted truth; she could think for herself. Elizabeth claimed, she deserved her own wealth. Rebecca spoke truly, witchdom denied. Mary was Baptist, original sin is a lie. Phillis proclaimed her race was the same. Jane grasped a girl's right, to write her own name. For females our Abigail representation called; when denied by her man, like Sally, was galled.

Lucy told true, Beecher bedded her too. Louisa lived life, no husband her to rule. Victoria published, down men's throats she rammed: We all sleep with each other, hypocrisy be damned. Dorothea's declaration was *Wake Up and Live! Becoming A Writer* was a gift she could give. In marriage our Laura refused to obey; her mother, she was honest, feared Indians in her day. Sarah, in a world of all men, wrote, taught, and published, living by the pen.

Margaret, our hero, for all women fought; our bodies are our own, not men's to be bought. I join my fellows, we've traveled through time, now speaking up loudly, sometimes in rhyme!

We will speak our truth.
We shall see it written.
Others will write
of secrets once hidden.

Over girls of the world,
our spirits hover,
encouraging always
a throw-back of covers.

Freedom, not fear,
for all, for the taking.
Words uncloak
new worlds in the making.

We women aren't witches
unveils a beginning.
Accept our choices
as rights, not sinning.

Join us in choosing
fifty-fifty for all.
True representation
in government halls.

GEG is a gain,
no one loses.
Justice prevails,
each for self chooses.

2019

WHITE FEATHERED FORM TURNS TO muscled brown body. Eyes of gold now gleam warm brown. Sixteen souls, travelers through four centuries time, gasp at this mighty transformation. Plumage rests discarded on warm earth, save discreet coverage below a finely formed waist. Shadow has swelled from small companion to tall, comely inamorato.

Joy's moment has arrived. Rising to stand on the towering rock, she casts a girlish gaze below. Blue eyes blaze with excitement, as all drink in the sight of her trembling suitor. With hand outstretched, he begs her troth.

Parting of grey skies above sends glowing sunlight to firmament at the clearing's edge. In the face of this magical moment, murmurs sound. Lifting from stone perch, our eager bride makes flight to a soft landing spot near the bordering wood. Hands touch, eyes meet, raised face to bent head yields union of quivering lips. At last.

Glances linger where two figures disappeared among ancient trees. Primaeval forest, in her depth, gifts lovers their thrilling seclusion.

Anne, Elizabeth, Rebecca, Mary. Phillis, Jane, Abigail, Sally. Lucy, Louisa, Victoria, Dorothea. Laura, Sarah, Margaret, Cid. All return to the task at hand. How to turn Joy's message from mere hope to human triumph? A Constitutional Amendment! Their draft is in progress.

Their long voyage through time has tightly bound this female forum. Witness to centuries past informs. Knowledge is power. Gender equal government shall come to be. Shipwreck of their mission is not what this congress has in mind, for themselves or any fellow beings.

Belief in a more perfect union is their guide. All women, and all men, are created equal, and shall be equally represented in each branch of government. This they know to be true.

Meantime, faint sounds from afar conjure flashes of fond memory. A gleam in each eye pairs with her own private, treasured moments. Life on earth is hard, but love brings handsome rewards. All here this day on Clark's Island share precious, consummate joy, as a message emerges from wooded glen. "All is right with the world," this missive seems to say.

Ears perk and smiles grace the corner of lips. All hear the muffled giggles, mounting chuckles, merge with soft moans of pleasure.

DRAFT OF EQUAL GENDER AMENDMENT

For purposes of this Amendment to the Constitution of the United States of America, there are two gender categories: female (XX) and male (XY).

Each gender is hereby granted fifty percent representation in each branch of federal government: in (first) our Congress (House of Representatives and Senate); in (second) our Executive (Presidency, Vice Presidency, Cabinet, and related positions); and in (third) our Judiciary (Supreme Court and all other federal judicial levels).

For each currently existing such position, whether held by a male or female, a second seat or position shall be established for the opposite gender, to be filled by vote or in similar manner to that used for the prior single position or seat. As a result, and as shall be required, for each seat or position designated male, there will be another seat or position designated female:

Following the establishment of two seats or positions where previously there was one:

Each political party nominating candidates for the House of Representatives shall be entitled to nominate a female for the first of two seats from each congressional district (hereby known as the female seat or representative); each political party nominating candidates for the House of Representatives shall be entitled to also nominate a male for the second of two seats from each congressional district (hereby known as the male seat or representative).

Each political party nominating candidates for the Senate shall be entitled to nominate a female for two seats from each state (hereby known as the female seats or senators); each political party nominating candidates for the House of Representatives shall be entitled to also nominate a male for two seats from each state (hereby known as the male seats or senators).

Each political party nominating candidates for President of the USA shall be entitled to nominate a female for the position hereby known as The Female President of the United States of America (FPOTUS); each political party nominating candidates for President of the USA shall be entitled to nominate a male for the position hereby known as The Male President of the United States of America (MPOTUS). FPOTUS and MPOTUS shall have rights and responsibilities exactly equal to the existing rights and responsibilities of the existing position of President of the United States of America.

Each political party nominating candidates for Vice President of the USA shall be entitled to pair a VP candidate with each nominee (male and female) for President. Each nominated pair must be gender equal, such that no pair is an all-male or all-female nomination.

When nominating candidates for cabinet level seats in the federal government (Secretaries of State, Defense, Labor, Interior, and any other existing departments of state), the FPOTUS and MPOTUS must join in presenting an agreed upon nominee to Female Secretary of State (FSOS), and Male Secretary of State (MSOS), and proceed in similar manner for each department of state.

When filling the newly created seats for Female or Male Justice of the Supreme Court of the United States of America the FPOTUS and MPOTUS must join in presenting to Congress an agreed upon nominee of the same gender as the position created.

When nominating candidates for vacated seats in the Supreme Court of the United States of America, the FPOTUS and MPOTUS must join in presenting to Congress an agreed upon nominee of the same gender as the position vacated . . .

. . . to be continued . . .

(We authors are ready to pass the torch to 21st century souls, confident in your abilities to carry on where we have left off.)

2020 JOY

THAT WARM DAY IN AUGUST 2019!

At the foot of Pulpit Rock, sixteen women, and my dear Shadow, had gathered a forty-ninth and last time. We had reviewed, once again, four centuries of women and men in America. Tales told by Luna had proved true. Her spirit, as always, warmed our hearts.

Off we went, Shadow and I, to reap our rewards. Our message delivered, our mission complete, sixteen ladies set to work, planning goals for institutions.

With a long road ahead, they'd need help from the world. So, one last effort from my new mate, Shadow, and from me, Luna's Joy. This also we leave, for twenty-first century employ.

A plea to one and all. Move onward. Move forward. Enter the Land of GEG.

Ode to the Land of GEG

Religion defined?
People joining together,
with organized head,
choosing views of life,
for the living,
for the dead.

Beyond religion,
but still in collusion,
people join now together,
in organized institution.

Choosing methods to govern,
our body politic views,
our polarized parties,
choosing view one,
Or view two.

We must choose to be kind,
from the Left they cry.
We must choose to be mean,
Far Right replies.
We must choose to respect,
some Left postulate.
We must choose to demean,
some Right remonstrate.

Such simple-minded views,
tempt the lazy to choose,
one or the other,
win or lose.

Keep women out.
No, let women in.
Abortion's a choice.
No, I say it's a sin.
She should decide.
No, I must deride,
as my God is my guide.

A Trumpian world,
took over the state:
Choose love?
No, choose hate.
Be kind?
No, be great.

This sad sense makes,
if just men in charge,
with none small in size,
with only the large.

Yet sea change is due,
a whole new view,
small and large together,
where one, now two.

Gender equal government,
fifty-fifty, the score.
Equal right to choose,
then all will have more.

Made in the USA
Middletown, DE
29 December 2020